MODERN MILITARY SERIES

ARTILLERY

MODERN MILITARY SERIES
Editor Michael Leitch

ARTILLERY

by Curt Johnson
Introduction by Aram Bakshian, Jr

octopus

First published in 1975 by Octopus Books Limited
59 Grosvenor Street, London W1
ISBN 0 7064 0411 4
© *1975 Octopus Books Limited*
Distributed in Australia by Rigby Limited
30 North Terrace, Kent Town, Adelaide, South Australia 5067
Produced by Mandarin Publishers Limited
14 Westlands Road, Quarry Bay, Hong Kong
Printed in Hong Kong

Reprinted 1976

JACKET FRONT *A German railway gun in action during
World War II: its slow rate of fire was offset by the
element of surprise.*
JACKET BACK *The lethal pawns of war on display in
Vietnam.*
HALF TITLE *A British 4·7-inch naval gun in World
War I.*
TITLE PAGE *A US gun crew at Fire Base Carroll,
Vietnam.*
THIS PAGE *A captured German 21-cm howitzer
photographed with its captors in the Ardennes in
November 1918.*

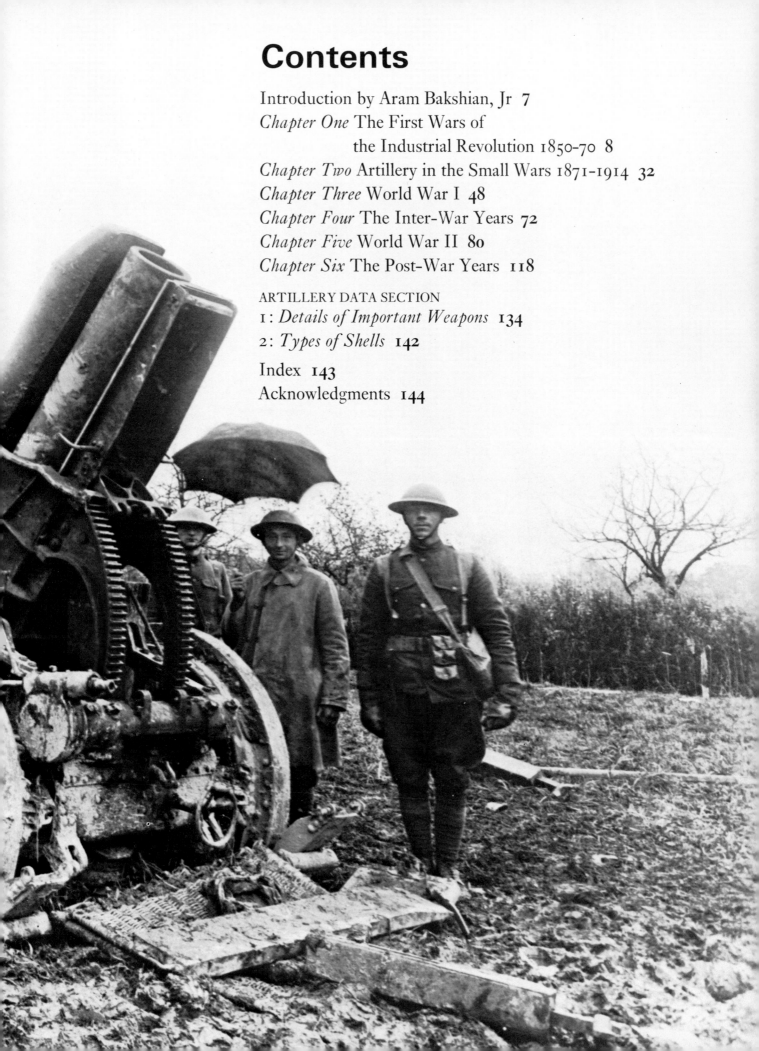

Contents

Introduction

by Aram Bakshian, Jr

The importance of artillery has been emphasized by figures as dramatically opposed to each other – in both temperament and military outlook – as Joseph Stalin and Hermann Goering. It was Stalin who once remarked that artillery was the 'god of war', and the inappropriately adipose Goering who exhorted the German people to remember that 'Guns will make us powerful; butter will only make us fat'. Nor is it surprising to recall that the greatest of modern captains, Napoleon Bonaparte, began his military life as a humble gunner cadet. He never forgot his early training. Throughout his career he proved a masterful artillerist, a commander who, in the apt phrase of Victor Hugo, massed and aimed his cannon 'like a single pistol'.

Despite the importance of artillery in earlier wars, it was not until the middle of the 19th century that drastic technical improvements began to be made – and rapidly – and it is from that time, beginning with the Crimean War, that the author of this book, Curt Johnson, takes up the history of artillery. His narrative of its evolution is not without its controversial passages. Johnson debunks the reputation of the famous 'Big Berthas', crowning pride of the Krupp works, and he suggests that the French '75' also enjoyed an inflated reputation in World War I. But he backs up his assertions with facts and figures and one is inclined, after sifting the evidence, to agree with him.

Artillery is a welcome addition to the Octopus Modern Military Series, a comprehensive collection of works on air, land and sea weaponry of the 'modern' or post-industrial period represented by approximately the last 100 years. The scope, detail and accuracy of *Artillery* will make it an invaluable acquisition for readers with a strong or casual interest in recent military history, and its many photographs, paintings and diagrams lend it a special value for modellers.

Considered in its earliest days a 'black art' akin to alchemy and witchcraft, gunnery and its practitioners sought a measure of respectability by adopting a patron saint, Saint Barbara. Today this connection with the occult, the sinister, has resurfaced with the almost satanic destructive force of the modern descendants of Shakespeare's 'vile guns'.

From the cannon at Sebastopol in 1854–55 to the self-propelled guns and missiles of our time, *Artillery* gives us the history of that most complex of the three original military branches. Smoothbore and rifle, mortar and missile, the history is an engrossing one, the closing chapter of which has yet to be written.

For at a time when the missile has been widely touted as the weapon of the future, we have seen old-fashioned North Vietnamese anti-aircraft guns take a deadly toll on American aircraft. And a few years earlier, in 1967, the world witnessed outnumbered Israeli forces, using a blend of air preponderance and superior tank and artillery tactics, inflict a humiliating defeat on Arab troops backed by the most sophisticated Soviet weaponry. Then in the desert war of 1973 the surface-to-air missiles of the Egyptian Army struck at Israeli aircraft with telling force. No one, indeed, in laboratories and war colleges around the globe, can be sure what new directions the ancient art of gunnery may be about to take.

But whatever these directions may be, there is no doubt about one thing. Whenever and wherever the next conflict begins, one of the first sounds to be heard will be a 'cannon's opening roar' not that much unlike the one described by Byron a century and a half ago at Waterloo.

OPPOSITE *German heavy artillery pounds Sebastopol during the siege of 1942.*

Chapter One

The First Wars of the Industrial Revolution 1850–70

The decade or so following the Crimean War may be regarded as the gestation period of modern ordnance. It begins with late smooth-bore muzzle-loaders, like the 'Napoleon', in the ascendant, and ends with rifled breech-loaders being adopted by most nations for their field artillery.

Until the mid-19th century ordnance development had been slow if not, at times, barely perceptible. Then suddenly, under the impetus of industrial and scientific progress, startling advances were made. In the Crimean War (1853–56), the belligerents experimented but briefly with rifled artillery; whereas six years later, in the American Civil War (1861–65), half the field artillery employed by the Union Army was rifled.

The Confederate Army, moreover, acquired and used a number of rifled guns with breech-loading mechanisms; the days of the muzzle-loader were numbered. By the Franco-Prussian War (1870–71), the Prussian field artillery was composed wholly of breech-loaders. And within a few years every Western nation was equipped with artillery comparable to that of the Prussians in 1870.

During the Napoleonic Wars, at the turn of the century, there had been a firm balance between each of the three principal arms–infantry, cavalry and artillery. But if any one of the three was a dominant force on the battlefield, then that arm was the artillery, whose powers could be exploited in various ways. For example, one of Napoleon's favourite tactics was to have his batteries unlimber in front

ARTILLERY TYPES

This table describes the chief functions of the principal artillery types in use in the mid-19th century. The range figures are those of representative US types in 1861: the gun is a Parrott 10-pounder field rifle at 5 degrees elevation; the howitzer is a Navy Dahlgren 12-pounder rifle at 5 degrees elevation, and the mortar is a 38-inch siege piece.

TYPE	USE	RANGE IN YARDS	TYPE OF FIRE	AMMUNITION
Gun (or cannon)	anti-personnel counter-battery	2,000	'direct' flat trajectory high velocity	canister shot shell spherical case (shrapnel)
Howitzer	anti-personnel against works and matériel	1,770	'searching' mid-trajectory medium velocity	canister shell spherical case incendiary
Mortar	anti-personnel against works and matériel	1,837	'dropping' high trajectory low velocity	shell spherical case incendiary
Gun-howitzer (or licorne)	combines the function of the gun and the howitzer			

Learning from another nation's conflict: foreign observers of the American Civil War are photographed with Union officers. Lying in the centre is Count von Zeppelin, the Prussian later noted for his pioneering work with airships; to his left is a Swedish Army officer, Lieutenant Rosencranz.

of a line of enemy infantry beyond the effective range of their smooth-bore muskets (200 yards or less). Once there, the French batteries would blast a hole in the enemy line using case shot (grape and canister). Then a column of French infantry would pour through the gap to exploit the breakthrough.

After the Napoleonic Wars came the introduction of the rifled musket and the Minié bullet. These innovations gave the infantry a weapon which it could use to great effect against the artillery. The new weapon could kill at 1,000 yards and was accurate at up to 600 yards. As one contemporary analyst put it: 'The relation long subsisting between field artillery and small arms became disturbed at once. Small arms experienced a vast accession to their power, whilst the powers of artillery remained nearly the same.'

It was clear that field artillery could no longer maintain its former dominant role in the offensive; from now on rifle fire from enemy infantry could pick off gunners and teams before their guns could be brought into battery at effective range. Indeed, it seemed that it might be the lot of the artillery to assume a secondary defensive role.

What in fact happened, though, was that tactical doctrine did not immediately follow the advances in weaponry. The infantry of most nations continued to use the dense formations of the Napoleonic Wars. This allowed the artillery to play a formidable role with long-range shell fire. Also, until the introduction of good smokeless powder (*c.* 1884), the first salvoes left the field covered in black smoke, which made aimed fire at best haphazard. In this situation the cannon's hitting power at close ranges was greatly valued.

SOME ARTILLERY DEFINITIONS

Smooth-bore. The interior of the barrel is smooth. With the exception of grape and canister (which are collections of shot packed respectively in sacks or metal containers), only round projectiles with a diameter smaller than that of the bore may be fired from smooth-bore guns. Because of this windage (space) the projectile 'bounces' down the barrel and emerges from the gun with less velocity and less predictable accuracy than a projectile fired from a rifle.

Rifle. The bore of the gun is machined with spiralling grooves that impart a spin to the projectile, which is usually long and pointed; this method increases accuracy, range and velocity.

Muzzle-loader. A gun loaded from the front of the tube.

Breech-loader. A gun loaded from the rear (breech) of the tube. The charge and projectile (or cartridge) is introduced into the chamber when the breech-block is open. The opening is then sealed behind the charge by means of a sliding-wedge or screw mechanism.

US 12-pounder 'Napoleon' gun-howitzer M-1857

The 'Napoleon', destined to be the most-used and most popular field gun of the American Civil War, was designed in 1853 by Louis Napoleon, the French ruler. It represents the high-point of smooth-bore gun development: in particular it was lighter than its contemporaries of the same calibre and, therefore, easier to handle.

In defence it was an awesome weapon, firing great shot-gun blasts of canister (tin cans filled with large lead balls) up to 400 yards. It also had good range, and could deliver spherical case (shrapnel) and shot to over 1,600 yards. Because rifled small arms had given the infantry a temporary ascendancy over smooth-bore field artillery, the defensive prowess of the Napoleon – its ability to hit hard at close range – made it well liked by Civil War artillerymen.

The US model was introduced for service in 1857. The Confederates, especially, used large numbers of Napoleons – which in their case were mostly captured pieces. The M-1857 was of bronze, but some Confederate copies were made of cast iron with reinforced breeches. This reinforcement was necessary because of the intrinsic weakness of cast iron as compared to bronze. The M-1857 smooth-bore 12-pounder remained in service with the US Army until the late 1870s.

Ammunition for the Napoleon

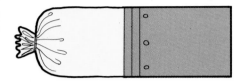

Cartridge bag, made of paper and tied at the head.

Tin case nailed to 'sabot' (wooden base); inside are 27 cast-iron shot.

Shown here is a typical 'fixed' round of canister; this type was used for close-range defensive work.

SPECIFICATIONS

Calibre	4·62 inches
Maximum range	1,619 yards at +5 degrees
	2,090 yards at +10 degrees firing shot
Length of bore	63·6 inches
Length of piece	72·6 inches
Weight of tube	1,230 pounds
Weight of carriage	1,128 pounds
Windage (difference between diameter of bore and diameter of projectile)	·01 inch
Powder charge	2 pounds (canister)
	2·5 pounds (shell, case and solid shot)
Weight of projectile	9·52 pounds (shell)
	12·17 pounds (case)
	14·80 pounds (canister)
	12·75 pounds (solid shot)
Muzzle velocity	1,486 fps (solid shot)
	1,495 fps (case)
	1,680 fps (shell)
Rate of fire	2 rpm (aimed)
	4 rpm (canister)
Firing mechanism	friction primer

Implements used by Civil War gunners

Handspikes, used for levering the gun into a firing position.

Gunner's quadrant, for gauging elevation.

Priming wire, for pricking the cartridge bag.

Rammer, sponge head and stave.

Worm, used to clear obstructions in the barrel.

Tangent scale, another method of measuring elevation; each step denoted a given range.

To operate the Napoleon, its crew first manoeuvred the piece into position. On the command 'Load', the No. 1 gunner drove the sponge down the bore, while No. 2 collected a cartridge from No. 5. No. 1 then removed the sponge, and the cartridge was inserted into the bore and seated firmly in the breech with the rammer. Meanwhile the No. 3 gunner had stopped the vent with his thumb (protected by a leather thumbstall) to prevent a premature discharge caused by smouldering combustible material which might have escaped the sponge during swabbing. Next the gunner placed the priming wire in the vent, pricking through the cartridge bag into the powder. The gun's elevation was corrected by means of a sighting device, and the friction tube was attached to one end of the lanyard. On the command 'Fire', the lanyard was pulled, igniting the charge and dispatching the projectile towards its target.

The Crimean War

The battles of the Crimean War were confused, scrambling affairs sometimes described as 'soldiers' battles', which means, in effect, that the generals were not directing them. In most of these actions the role of artillery was limited, but it did play a central part in the most important event of the war, the epic siege of Sebastopol.

Sebastopol had been the most important Russian naval base and arsenal on the Black Sea since the late 18th century. Its coastal defence system, begun in 1783 and periodically improved, was considered impregnable by the standards of a brick-and-masonry age. In 1837 the Czar had ordered additional defences to be built behind the town, but nothing had been done. So, when war began in 1853, Sebastopol was defenceless on the landward, or southern, side. Eventually in April 1854, Colonel Frants Todleben, an engineer officer, was sent to the base to plan and supervise the building of land defences. But, because no one anticipated an attack on Sebastopol from behind the town, Todleben took his time. Then, on 13 September, a British and French Allied army

BELOW *A scene in the British mortar battery at the Siege of Sebastopol. It shows the gunner at right pouring bursting powder into a hollow spherical shell. Behind him two gunners ram a* propellant charge down the bore of their mortar, while to the rear of the piece a comrade holds his thumb over the vent to stop a premature detonation of the charge.*

ABOVE LEFT *A Quiet Night in the Batteries, by William Simpson.*
ABOVE *Gunners at work on mortars behind the British Right*
Attack at Sebastopol; from a painting published in May 1855.

began to land at Old Fort some 30 miles away to the north. After defeating Prince Menshikov's Russian army at the Alma on 20 September, the Allies crossed the River Belbek and came within sight of the northern defences of Sebastopol. There they found Todleben's recently constructed Star Fort; considering this too strong to assault, they turned and marched around the town towards the southern defences.

To the south of the harbour, Todleben's works were still very weak. General Cathcart, commanding the British 4th Division, described them as consisting of a martello tower and a 'low park wall not in good repair'. Clearly, Sebastopol could have been taken by storm at that moment, but while the Russians prepared for the worst, the Allied assault was called off. The anticipated cost of an assault, estimated at 500 men, was considered too great. A great opportunity was thus allowed to slip away, and the Allies began formal siege operations.

In the meantime, Todleben had not been idle. He directed every civilian, soldier and sailor that could be found to the task of strengthening the flimsy southern

Sebastopol from the rear of the Malakoff. In the foreground are bomb-proofs in which Russian soldiers sheltered from the Allied bombardment. In the harbour (right centre) may be seen the remains of the pontoon bridge over which the Russian army escaped to the northern side of the harbour.

defences. Since he did not have time to construct permanent, brick-and-masonry forts of the type that had been the mainstay of the defensive for centuries,[1] Todleben built a formidable system of earthen bastions, connecting trenches and supporting batteries. By mid-October, Sebastopol was

---

[1] The methods of fortifying a town had changed little since the days of Sébastien de Vauban (1633–1707), the French siege-master.

one of the most formidable fortresses in the world. The older coastal defences mounted 533 guns. Todleben's earthworks mounted 60 guns to the north of the harbour and 145 on the southern defences. There were, altogether, nearly 3,000 heavy guns (including those of the fleet) available for the defences, but most of these were stored because there was simply no place to put them.

The Allies, for their part, had managed rapidly to put together a siege train, and, on 17 October 1854 the Russians felt the first impact of the greatest artillery bombardment in the history of the world to that time. Beginning at dawn 126 Allied guns, most of them sited in three great batteries, began to pound the Russian earthworks.

Formidable as this fire was, the defenders replied with tremendous vigour. Most of the Russian batteries were manned by sailors who fired their guns 'in broadside', that is, all at once, as if they were firing from the gun deck of a man-o'-war. The effect was devastating. At 10.30 am the Russians destroyed one of the magazines of the French batteries firing from Mount Rodolph. Later a caisson was hit. The French commander, finding the fire too hot,

'invited' his gunners to shelter. Not one declined and by noon the French batteries were silent. After that, the fire of the English batteries became an exercise in futility. The Russians were without doubt the stronger party: they eventually fired 20,000 rounds to the Allies' 9,000. What is more, their works were undamaged.

The October bombardment was but a meagre foretaste of things to come. Other bombardments followed, some of which attained titanic dimensions; one such was the Easter bombardment which began on 8 April 1855 and lasted 11 days.

During each day of the Easter bombardment the Russian works were destroyed, but each night the gallant defenders restored them. Anticipating an assault at any time, the Russian commanders packed their men into dugouts and bombproofs. No assault came, and they lost 6,000 men in the bombardment. Still they persevered, and replied to the Allied bombardment with 88,000 shells from their own batteries.

On 7 June 1855 the French took the Mamelon, an important work close to the main Russian line. Todleben had

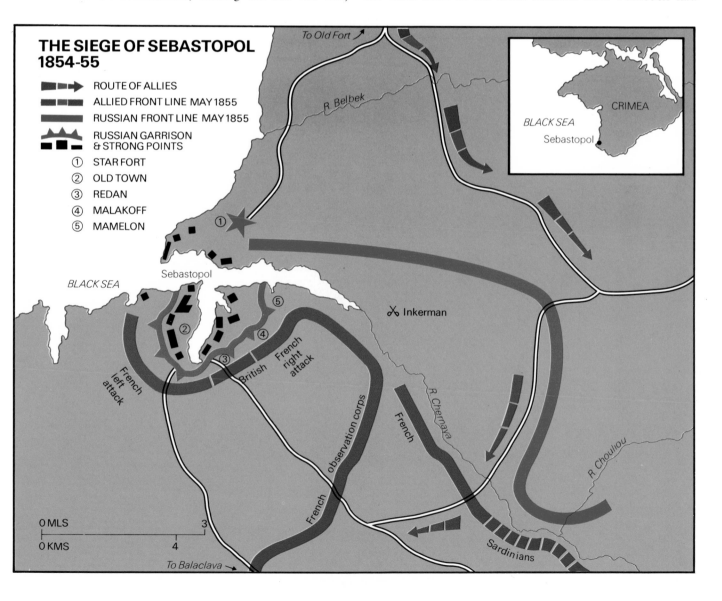

THE SIEGE OF SEBASTOPOL 1854-55

- ROUTE OF ALLIES
- ALLIED FRONT LINE MAY 1855
- RUSSIAN FRONT LINE MAY 1855
- RUSSIAN GARRISON & STRONG POINTS
- ① STAR FORT
- ② OLD TOWN
- ③ REDAN
- ④ MALAKOFF
- ⑤ MAMELON

To Old Fort

R. Belbek

CRIMEA

BLACK SEA

Sebastopol

BLACK SEA

Sebastopol

Inkerman

French left attack

British

French right attack

French observation corps

French

R. Chernaya

R. Chouliou

Sardinians

0 MLS   3
0 KMS   4

To Balaclava

foreseen that this might happen and, after the Easter bombardment, he had constructed a new work, the Malakoff. Situated behind the Mamelon, the Malakoff commanded the Russian line and the town and, together with a strong work flanking it known as the Redan, held the key to Sebastopol. All the efforts of the Allies were naturally directed towards taking these two works.

The daily bombardments of the Allies increased in intensity, culminating in a tremendous three-day bombardment (5–8 September 1855). The Russians suffered terribly, especially in the last month. Prince Gorchakov, the Russian commander, reported that his casualties were 500–1,000 men per day during that period. The Malakoff was irreparably damaged, and the Redan reduced to a jagged heap. Finally, on 8 September, British and French infantry rushed the two forts. The British were repulsed at the Redan, but the French carried the Malakoff. This determined the fate of Sebastopol. Gorchakov blew up the town and withdrew his men across a pontoon bridge to the northern side of the harbour.

The casualties in the siege of Sebastopol, which had lasted nearly a year, were over 300,000 men. The artillery, crude as it was, had contributed mightily to that toll, especially among the Russians who persisted in massing their men in the trenches during each bombardment. In forts like the Malakoff enormous bomb-proofs had been constructed to shelter the infantry needed to repel attacks, but even these were not sufficient to protect the numbers of men that the Russians crowded into the trenches. And when the Allies gained artillery superiority, as they did during the Easter bombardment, there was little the Russians could do, despite frantic rebuilding, to prevent the steady deterioration of their works. At the end of the siege there were only a few serviceable gun carriages left in Sebastopol, and the forts were formless piles of rubble.

Most of the projectiles thrown into Sebastopol were spherical shot and shell. Shot was solid and was used for battering. A shell consisted of a hollow sphere containing a small bursting charge; it was used against personnel rather than earthworks, where its fragments had little effect. The fuse used with shell was a time fuse, usually ignited by the flash of the propellant powder. Another type of projectile

used was red-hot shot. This was shot heated in a furnace prior to firing and carried to the gun with tongs. It was used for its incendiary effect, as were 'carcasses', projectiles which were pierced with holes and fired from howitzers and mortars.

Sebastopol produced few innovations. Some rifled guns –most notably the British 68-pounder oval-bore Lancaster gun–were briefly experimented with, but the results of these tests were unsatisfactory. Otherwise, it is worth noting only that the Russians had some success using cast-iron gun-carriages on a few of their heavy pieces; these were found to make working the guns easier.

Altogether the Allied artillery fired 1,250,000 projectiles into the Russian fortress. The remarkable strength of the Russian earthworks in the face of this storm of shot and shell seems to have been overlooked by most military men of the time. Certainly, the day of the brick fort was past. This was conclusively demonstrated on 16 October 1855, when three French steam-powered floating batteries engaged and demolished the Russian forts at Kinburn on the Bug River after a three-hour bombardment.

OPPOSITE *The Barrack Battery at Sebastopol. Note the rope mantelets at the gun embrasures and around the gun tubes: their function was to protect the gunners from small-arms fire.*
BELOW *The interior of the Redan, showing some of the sandbags and gabions (wickerwork cylinders) that were essential parts of Todleben's improvised fortifications. Most of the guns in the Russian works were naval pieces taken from the vessels of the Black Sea Fleet.*

The American Civil War

As we mentioned earlier, the Union Army used large numbers of rifled guns during the American Civil War. By 1863 about half the Union Army's field artillery was rifled. Then, however, the ratio dropped, and during the last two years of the war only about one-third of the field artillery was rifled. This happened because, for various reasons, rifling had brought no worthwhile advantage over the Confederate artillery, which was largely equipped with smooth-bores.

One important factor was the nature of the countryside over which the war was fought. There was simply not much point in employing rifles in wooded, half-cultivated areas. Even when rifles could be employed at great ranges, however, the small amount of bursting powder in their shells and the uncertainty of the fuses made them less than fully effective. Also, as soon as the infantry learned to adopt open formations and to advance in rushes using all available cover, long-range fire lost its potency.

At First Bull Run (21 July 1861) two fine batteries of US regular artillery, those of Ricketts and Griffin, equipped

ABOVE *A Confederate Whitworth 12-pounder breech-loading rifle with the breech-block open. It had a range of nearly six miles.*
BELOW *The Great Gun at White Point Battery, Charleston, South Carolina, as depicted by Conrad Wise Chapman in October 1863.*
OPPOSITE *Battery Marion at Charleston, recorded by Conrad Wise Chapman in a watercolour dated November 1863.*

with 10 10-pounder Parrott rifles and two 12-pounder howitzers, engaged a Confederate battery of four 6-pounder smooth-bore guns under the command of John G. Imboden. This contest, a classic battle of rifled cannon versus smooth-bores, was conducted at ranges of from 1,000–1,500 yards. The Confederate battery more than held its own despite the disparity in numbers, and this led Imboden to conclude that:

In open ground, at 1,000 yards, a 6-pounder battery of smooth guns, or, at 1,500 to 1,800 yards, a similar battery of 12-pounder Napoleons, well handled, will in one hour discomfit double the number of the best rifles ever put in the field.

This is not to say that the fire of the rifled batteries had been inaccurate. It was, in fact, so accurate that Imboden confessed that 'hundreds of shells from these fine rifle-guns exploded in front of and around my battery on that day . . .' But, without exception, the high-velocity shells had buried themselves in the ground before exploding, and no one was hurt; later, when Imboden viewed the position occupied by his battery, he remarked that 'the ground looked as though it had been rooted up by hogs'.

But if the offensive capability of field artillery in the American Civil War was somewhat dubious, there was no questioning the potency of a line of guns in defence. Certainly the infantry feared an encounter with massed guns more than any other battlefield circumstance.

At Malvern Hill (1 July 1862) the Union chief of artillery, Colonel Henry J. Hunt, placed nearly 100 guns hub-to-hub on rising ground with about half a mile of open ground between them and the Confederate infantry. The Confederates had 14 brigades of infantry prepared for an assault. Their artillery, which was to have supported the infantry, then attempted to deploy. As each battery was wheeled separately into position, up to 50 Union guns opened fire. In the inferno that followed, battery after battery of the Confederate artillery was wrecked.

Late in the afternoon the Confederate infantry emerged from the woods to attack. Confusion, caused as much by poor maps as by the broken ground to their front, upset the rhythm of the attack, and the 14 brigades went in piecemeal, as the artillery had before them. As each column in succession left the woods and began to climb the slope, every gun that could be brought to bear, including the siege guns farther back, opened a deadly fire. Shells alone were enough

to destroy most of the columns, canister being used against those brave bands of survivors who actually pressed up to the guns. Nearly half the Confederate casualties at Malvern Hill were in fact caused by artillery fire – a proportion which the Confederate General, Harvey Hill, described as 'unprecedented' in the annals of warfare.

During the Civil War massed artillery firing from a distance was used on several occasions to prepare the way for an infantry assault. At Gettysburg (1–3 July 1863), for example, the massed fire of 159 Confederate guns under Colonel E. P. Alexander was intended to prepare the way for the famous assault of 15,000 Confederate infantry (now known as 'Pickett's Charge'). The principal aim of the Confederate barrage was not to break up or destroy the infantry formations waiting to receive the attack, but rather to neutralize or force the withdrawal of the Union guns on Cemetery Ridge. If this could not be done, it was reckoned that perhaps the Union guns would exhaust their long-range ammunition in reply, and much the same object would be achieved.

But on the Ridge itself the crews of some 80 Union guns, grouped under the overall command of General Hunt, were

OPPOSITE *Col E. P. Alexander, above, who directed the Confederate guns at Gettysburg. Below is a Union siege battery near Charleston; the guns are Parrott 100-pounder rifles.*
ABOVE *James Hope's painting of the Battle of Antietam shows Union infantry being shelled by Stephen Dill Lee's battery.*
BELOW *A 15-inch Rodman gun photographed in Battery Rodgers near Hunting Creek on the Potomac River.*

instructed to hold their reply fire for about 20 minutes. This was done in order to conserve ammunition for the assault which everyone expected to follow.

Alexander's grand battery fired on the Union line from 1 pm to 2.45 pm on the afternoon of 3 July. A few Union batteries on the forward slope of Cemetery Ridge (the

US 3-inch Ordnance Rifle

The 3-inch Ordnance rifle was a lightweight rifled gun manufactured in large numbers during the American Civil War by Rodman and supplied to the field and horse artillery of the Union Army. It was made of wrought iron and was especially noted for its accuracy: one gunner was heard to boast that his 3-inch rifle could 'hit the top of a barrel at a mile'.

A similar rifled gun, the Parrott 10-pounder, had been developed earlier with a calibre of 2·90 inches; in due course the Parrotts were rebored to take ammunition identical to that of the 3-inch gun. The Ordnance rifle was issued to field units from late 1863. It remained in service until the Spanish-American War of 1898.

The aerial view below emphasizes the almost deceptively simple lines of a gun that by repute was deadly accurate at a one-mile range and remained effective at twice that distance. In the side view the nearside wheel is omitted to show more clearly the respective sizes of carriage and gun tube, and how they fitted together. The wooden stock of the carriage served to connect it to the limber and was used to direct the piece. Its lower portion, the trail, rested on the ground when the gun was unlimbered; the ring at the end of the trail, the lunette, received the pintle hook by which the limber was attached. Also shown is the lock chain: fixed to the side of the trail, it was used to keep the wheel from turning.

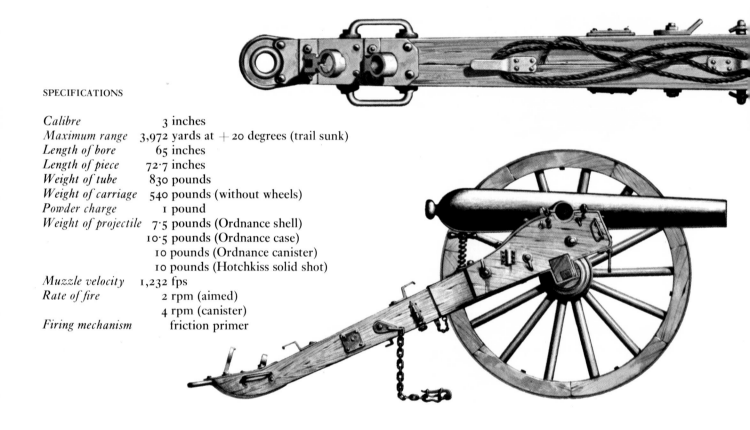

SPECIFICATIONS

Calibre	3 inches
Maximum range	3,972 yards at + 20 degrees (trail sunk)
Length of bore	65 inches
Length of piece	72·7 inches
Weight of tube	830 pounds
Weight of carriage	540 pounds (without wheels)
Powder charge	1 pound
Weight of projectile	7·5 pounds (Ordnance shell)
	10·5 pounds (Ordnance case)
	10 pounds (Ordnance canister)
	10 pounds (Hotchkiss solid shot)
Muzzle velocity	1,232 fps
Rate of fire	2 rpm (aimed)
	4 rpm (canister)
Firing mechanism	friction primer

The Barrel

The gun tube, weighing 830 pounds, rested between two pieces of wood reinforced with iron and known as cheeks (see also the larger view above). The trunnions (G) projecting from the barrel fitted into beds or depressions in the cheeks, and were held secure by iron capsquares.

A Cascabel
B Breech
C Bore
D Muzzle
E Body
F Chase
G Trunnion
H Rimbase

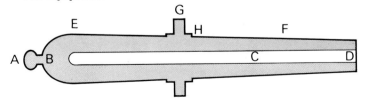

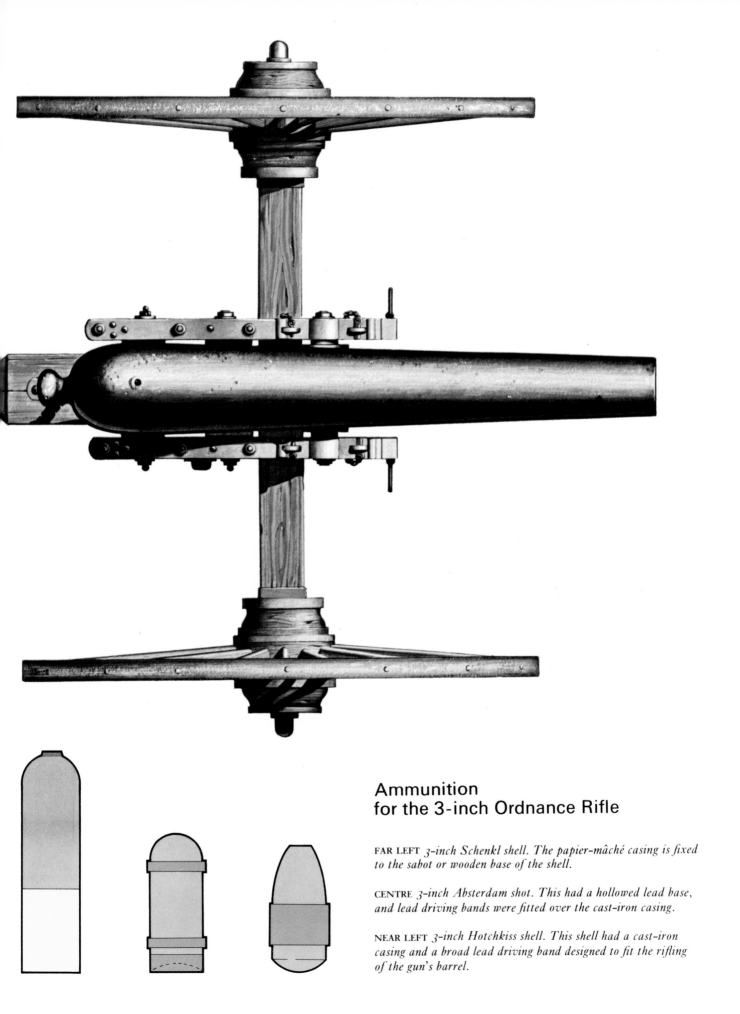

Ammunition
for the 3-inch Ordnance Rifle

FAR LEFT *3-inch Schenkl shell. The papier-mâché casing is fixed to the sabot or wooden base of the shell.*

CENTRE *3-inch Absterdam shot. This had a hollowed lead base, and lead driving bands were fitted over the cast-iron casing.*

NEAR LEFT *3-inch Hotchkiss shell. This shell had a cast-iron casing and a broad lead driving band designed to fit the rifling of the gun's barrel.*

objective) were wrecked, but most of the Confederate fire was long and fell behind the Ridge. On the Union side Hunt's orders were not completely followed: batteries along the line of the Union Second Corps were ordered to reply by General Hancock, the Corps commander. Hunt made his way towards this part of the line and ordered the firing to cease, but the guns had by then used up their long-range ammunition.

When Hancock's batteries stopped Alexander, believing his fire had silenced the Union guns, gave the signal for the assault to go in. As the Confederate infantry emerged from the line of trees and low ridges which had sheltered them, they were subjected to a devastating artillery fire. This fire was so effective that the Confederates began to 'drift' towards the safest point in the enemy lines. This, of course, was the position occupied by the non-firing Second Corps artillery, whose area was the only part of the Union line to be penetrated in the action. Later Hunt was to write that, had his instructions been followed completely, the assaulting column would have broken up in mid-course. As it was, no more than 300 of the 15,000 attackers reached the Union line.

Following the failure of the Confederate assault, there was pressure in the Union Army for an immediate advance on the mile-long gap in the Confederate line formerly occupied by the men of Pickett's assaulting column. At that point only Alexander's gunners, bravely maintaining their

line, seemed to block the way to a rout of Lee's Army. Even so, the mere sight of that line of guns was enough to dissuade even the most sanguine observer. Hunt, who knew too well what guns could do and had no way of knowing that Alexander's guns were without ammunition, described such a move as 'stark madness', and no counter-attack was made.

In the years leading up to the American Civil War, it had been generally accepted that in any ship-versus-shore duel the gunboat would be worsted. This was largely because of a system of horizontal shell-firing that had been devised in 1822 by a French General, Henri Paixhans (1783–1854). The exploding Paixhans shell, fired on a flat trajectory, blew up the old wooden-walled gunboats and made them obsolete. This was perhaps most graphically illustrated at the naval Battle of Sinope (1853), when a Russian squadron shelled and set on fire a Turkish squadron of seven frigates and five smaller ships.

A further well-established belief of the day was that brick fortresses – provided their foundations were protected by a glacis and their defenders adequately armed and pro-

water. This interior cooling put a permanent compressive strain on the metal surrounding the bore, and Rodman's monster 'columbiads', as they were called, were structurally much sounder (and therefore safer) than previous iron pieces. Rodman's biggest gun was a 20-inch muzzle-loading smooth-bore that fired a solid shot weighing 1,080 pounds.

Major Rodman (1815–71), an American ordnance specialist, also improved muzzle velocity with his invention of a progressive-burning powder, which was much more efficient than ordinary black powder. However, while Rodman's various innovations improved the efficiency and increased the size of smooth-bores, these guns were plainly outclassed as siege weapons by the new large-calibre rifles used during the American Civil War.

Several types of heavy rifled pieces were used during the Civil War, the most common being those built by Parrott, Brooke, Blakely and Armstrong. The safest were built-up types like the Armstrong 150-pounder. The breech of the Armstrong gun was reinforced by a series of 'hoops' of wrought iron which were shrunk-on over one another and the gun tube. At the other end of the spectrum were the Parrotts, cast-iron pieces with a wrought-iron reinforcing

OPPOSITE *The upper picture shows the breaches made in the brickwork of Fort Pulaski by General Quincy Gillmore's Union bombardment. In the lower picture a battery of Union field artillery is seen in the trenches near Petersburg, Virginia, in 1864.*
LEFT *A Confederate Armstrong 150-pounder muzzle-loading rifle at Fort Fisher near Wilmington, North Carolina.*

visioned – could resist the attempts of a besieger for months. The siege of Sebastopol had demonstrated the resilience of earthworks, too – though most military men remained convinced that proper brickwork forts would have served the Russians better.

In the meantime, the industrialization of war continued apace: most navies converted to steam propulsion, a few ironclads were launched and large-calibre rifled guns appeared. Eventually, by 1865, the situation was such that all previous thinking on siege and naval bombardment had to be completely revised.

Among the new siege weapons were large smooth-bores cast by Major T. J. Rodman's improved method of cooling the metal from the inside of the bore by a stream of running

band shrunk-on over the breech. Parrott guns were cheap and easy to make, but they frequently burst. After the naval bombardment of Fort Fisher near Wilmington, North Carolina, during which six Parrotts burst causing 45 casualties in the Union fleet, Admiral Porter pronounced them 'unfit for service, and calculated to kill more of our men than those of the enemy'.

If the new rifles were somewhat unpredictable, they were undeniably effective. No brick-and-masonry fort could stand for long against their fire. The best illustration of this is the brief siege of Fort Pulaski near Savannah, Georgia (10–11 April 1865). Fort Pulaski was a strong brick fort mounting 40 heavy guns either *en barbette* (to fire over the parapet) or enclosed in casemates. It was situated on an island at the mouth of the Savannah River. The nearest firm ground suitable for mounting siege-pieces to bear on the fort was on Tybee Island over a mile away. In the opinion of the Chief Engineer of the US Army, 'The work could not be reduced in a month's firing with any number of guns of manageable calibres.'

However, a Union force under General Quincy A. Gillmore went ahead and emplaced several heavy guns and mortars on Tybee Island; they began bombarding Pulaski at 8.15 am on 10 April. By 1.00 pm, in Gillmore's words: 'It could be seen that the rifled projectiles were surely eating their way into the scarp of the *pan-coupé* and adjacent south face.' By noon the next day two enormous breaches with an aggregate width of 30 feet had been opened in the southeast face, and Union shot was searching the interior of the fort. At 2.00 pm on the 11th, the Confederate garrison surrendered. The two-day bombardment of Fort Pulaski was the first time rifled heavy guns had been used against brickwork forts; more important still, those few hours of shelling had rendered every existing brickwork fort obsolete.

Inevitably, it took some time for this knowledge to penetrate the minds of European strategists. As late as 1870, for

example, General von Moltke and the Prussian 'technicians' counselled against besieging French cities protected by concentric rings of brick forts. But when the Prussians did take on French fortresses, their 15-cm guns and howitzers were surprisingly effective, especially the howitzers, which were used to breach 'invisible' scarps (out of sight beyond intervening glacis). This happened, for example, at Strasbourg; in the end, as a result of events in the Franco-Prussian War, all new forts were constructed of concrete and earth.

OPPOSITE *The Union Army's armoured railroad battery on General Grant's City Point Railroad near Petersburg, Virginia.*
LEFT *The 'Dictator', a famous heavy mortar that fired 45 rounds during the Siege of Petersburg. It was shunted about on a railway mount.*
BELOW *The naval bombardment of Fort Fisher near Wilmington, North Carolina, on 15 January 1865, as painted by Xanthus Russell Smith. At this period, before armour-piercing shot had been developed, steam-driven ironclad warships were able to engage forts with impunity. The monitors of the Union fleet shown here fired on the fort from 1,200 yards and drove the Confederate gunners into their bomb-proofs.*

The Prussians at War

In 1866 the Prussian Army entered its war against Austria with a mixture of old and new equipment that indicated a steady, if somewhat hesitant, transition from smooth-bore muzzle-loaders to rifled breech-loaders. Each Prussian army corps had a group of 16 batteries attached to it. Six of the 16 batteries were equipped with old smooth-bore muzzle-loaders, while the other 10 used the new Krupp steel breech-loaders. Of the smooth-bores it was said that, at 1,000 paces: 'The first shot is for the Devil, the second for God, and only the third for the King.' The Krupp rifles were 4- or 6-pounders. Despite its impressive equipment, however, the Prussian field artillery was comparatively inexperienced, having seen only limited action in the Danish War of 1864.

The Austrian artillery was equipped wholly with rifled muzzle-loaders. These guns were inferior to the Krupp breech-loaders in rapidity of fire; in addition, Austrian shells and fuses were often defective. Nevertheless, the Austrians had been taught a lesson by the French in 1859 (the Italian War) and in 1866 they were to prove themselves the better gunners time and again despite their material inferiority.

The problems of the Prussian field artillery in 1866 seem to have had more to do with leadership, tactics and lack of experience than with the guns themselves. While on the march the artillery was relegated to the rear of each column. In battle, those few pieces that were brought into the line (the greater part stayed among the reserves) were deployed here and there in no particular order, but generally as far to the rear as possible. There was no plan to replenish ammunition expended (this could be quite a problem with rapid-firing breech-loaders), and once a battery had fired its complement, it usually left the field. In consequence the Prussian infantry came to despise its artillery, which became more and more of an embarrassment as the campaign went on.

On the other hand the Austrian artillery fought brilliantly in each engagement, and nowhere more so than in the decisive Battle of Königgrätz (3 July 1866), where it covered the retreat of General von Benedek's army from successive positions. In its comments on this battle, the Prussian *Staff History* noted that 'the well-sustained fire of the powerful line of artillery . . . proved that part, at least, of the hostile army still retained its full power of resistance'.

There could be no mistaking the keen disappointment felt by Prussian artillerists at their dismal showing in 1866. The infantry had achieved glory, but the artillery met abuse at every turn. After the engagement at Bistritz Prince Friedrich Karl, commanding the Prussian First Army, had been heard to remark that his artillery 'was scarcely of more use . . . than it could have been at Berlin'. Clearly, some changes were in order.

By 1870 the artillery was completely equipped with Krupp rifles. Under the demanding eye of Inspector-General Gustav von Hindersin, tactical training reached a high degree of efficiency. A new *Abteilung* (brigade) system was introduced, in which the artillery was placed well to the front in the column of march. Groups of batteries were to go into action at the trot. There was to be no reserve – each battery was to push to the front as rapidly as possible and engage the enemy's guns in combat. The long-range duels of the Austrian War (up to 2,000 paces had been common) were rejected in favour of closer work. No longer were guns permitted to withdraw to replenish ammunition; instead an efficient system of supply was introduced.

The French Army which was to face the Prussians in 1870–71 was notably inferior in artillery. The French gunners were tactically competent, but their guns were mostly old bronze smooth-bores of the Lahitte type that had been rebored to take rifled ammunition. These guns were similar to the Austrian muzzle-loading rifles of 1866; even so, French gunnery was in practice less effective than that of the Austrians. The French, however, were counting on the Chassepot, their superior infantry rifle, and the *mitrailleuse*, a Gatling-like machine gun, to bring them victory.

In the first battles of the Franco-Prussian War the Prussian artillery, imbued with the von Hindersin spirit and eager to overcome the stigma of 1866, dashed into the open with the infantry – sometimes fighting right on the skirmish line. Inevitably, there were heavy casualties. According to Prince Kraft zu Hohenlohe-Ingelfingen, Chassepot fire 'battered' the gunners more than artillery fire, and it was not uncommon for whole batteries to be decimated by small arms fire as they went into action.

The French artillery, although hopelessly outclassed, was still able to play a few tricks on the Prussian zealots. At Gravelotte-St Privat, on 18 August 1870, the French guns duelled with 84 Prussian guns at 2,200 yards. When they found that they were having little effect on the French, the Prussians added more guns and closed to 1,650 yards. Suddenly, the French guns disappeared. A Prussian infantry assault went in; just as quickly, the French guns reappeared and destroyed the infantry. This bold piece of deceit forced the Prussians to close their gun-line to within 1,000 yards of the French position; there they deployed 192 guns and fired on the French guns for two hours before hazarding a further assault by the infantry.

At the Battle of Sedan (1 September 1870), the Prussians caught a large French army in a valley completely surrounded by hills. As the King of Prussia, Count von Bismarck, von Moltke and other distinguished persons watched from the heights, the massed fire of the Prussian field guns was turned on the enemy. At first the battle followed the pattern of Malvern Hill (1862). As the French struggled forward seeking a way out of the 'mouse trap', their formations were badly torn by shell fire. Then more

and more Prussian guns began to crowd into the gun line. Soon, four-fifths of the Prussian Army's artillery, nearly 600 guns in all, ringed Sedan. More counter-attacks were made. Each met the same fate. One French division sought refuge in the Bois de Garenne: instantly 540 guns were turned on the wood, and, from a distance, it appeared to be consumed in a blanket of flash and smoke. Finally, the French had had enough. Their army, numbering over 100,000 men, surrendered.

ABOVE *The Montigny* mitrailleuse, *the multi-barrelled machine gun with which the French hoped to surprise and destroy the Prussians in 1870.*

ABOVE *The devastated position of the Austrian Artillery Reserve after the Battle of Königgrätz (Sadowa) on 3 July 1866. During this engagement it was the stubborn fighting withdrawal of the Austrian artillery that saved General von Benedek's army from total destruction at the hands of von Moltke's Prussians.*
LEFT *Prussian artillery in the trenches before Strasbourg, 1870. The gun positions are flanked by protective gabions – wickerwork cylinders filled with earth.*
RIGHT *Krupp's Great (1,000-pounder) Gun, which the manufacturer presented to the King of Prussia. This illustration records the gun's appearance at the Paris Exhibition of 1867.*

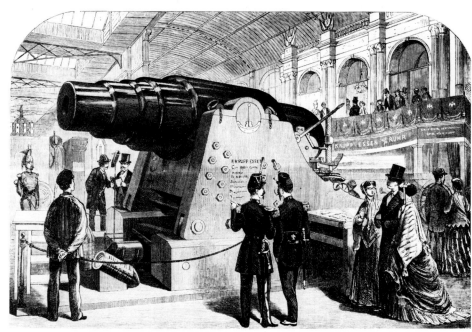

Chapter Two

Artillery in the Small Wars 1871–1914

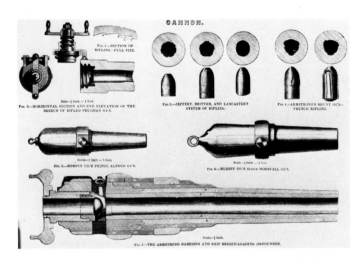

The period between, roughly, the end of the Franco-Prussian War (1871) and the outbreak of World War I (1914) was one of great upheaval in the realm of ordnance. The reputation of Prussian (or rather, German) arms was at its height, and a cult of imitation swept the West. Soldiers donned the *Pickelhaube* (spiked helmet) in places as far apart as Aldershot in England and Fort Leavenworth, Kansas. What the plain weight of experience had failed to do, the German 'cult' did. The most conservative nations soon adopted rifled breech-loaders for their field artillery, and German arms manufacturers like Krupp enjoyed windfall sales.

The first nation to replace its field artillery was France, which, of course, had had direct experience of Krupp's

ABOVE LEFT *A selection of cannon types developed for service in the latter part of the 19th century.*

LEFT *The Krupp firm's specially designed heavy gun transport.*

BELOW *One of the de Bange '90s' in a quiet sector of the Western Front in World War I. De Bange's 1877 design for a screw breech made these guns the most advanced of their day – though by 1914 they were obsolescent.*

OPPOSITE, TOP *Portable 2·95-inch and 3·45-inch breech-loading mortars, forerunners in Germany of the wartime Minenwerfer.*

rifled breech-loaders. The old Lahitte M-1859 rifled cannon-howitzer was supplanted in 1877 by the de Bange 90-mm field gun. The de Bange 'system', really a complete family of guns, had been adopted after intensive competition among French manufacturers. Reffye, Lahitolle, Orly and de Bange had all submitted designs, but de Bange won on the merits of his very advanced design for a screw breech with an obturation system utilizing an expansive pad of asbestos, tallow and paraffin plastic[1]. When one of de Bange's guns was fired, the force of the explosion pushed a mushroom-shaped steel head backwards against the asbestos pad, which flattened and sealed the breech against the escape of gases. Since the pad would melt only at very high temperatures, maintenance and wear were kept to a minimum.

[1] The problem of obturation, *i.e.* securing a gas-tight seal in the breech, had pre-occupied gunners since the cannon was first introduced to Western armies in the 14th century.

ABOVE RIGHT *A Krupp 4·13-inch fortress and siege gun L/35 with carriage; chocks were used to help stem the recoil.*
RIGHT *A Krupp employee works the elevating mechanism of a 2·95-inch field gun L/28.*
BELOW *German 11-inch coastal artillery. The crane at the rear hoisted shells and powder cartridges up to the breech.*

This very efficient system is the most commonly used today.

In 1860 it had appeared that Great Britain would lead the world in adopting the new rifled breech-loaders. Tests conducted by the Ordnance following the Crimean War had matched Armstrong guns against the unique hexagonal-bore guns of Joseph Whitworth. Whitworth's iron breech-loaders burst frequently (none lasted beyond the tenth round) and took half an hour to load. Armstrong's guns performed well, although the lead coating of the projectiles stripped away during firing. It was decided to convert to Armstrong's pattern, and 12-pounder breech-loaders were ordered for the field artillery. These guns were used in the Second Opium War (1856–60), and although there were few complaints about the guns' performance, it was found that in the heat of action many crews failed to close the breech properly, which led to terrible accidents. Later, in 1863, there were more tests. This time Whitworth submitted a rifled muzzle-loader, and Armstrong's guns were found inferior in every respect to the muzzle-loaders. The conversion to Armstrong guns was halted in 1867, and by 1870 it was decided to revert to muzzle-loaders. The new muzzle-loaders would, however, use Armstrong's three-groove system of rifling and fire an improved studded shell called the Woolwich pattern. Not until 1885 did Great Britain finally adopt rifled breech-loaders for her horse and field artillery.

The Krupp 28-cm heavy howitzer is towed to its firing position by motor car in two loads; the gun crew is shown accompanying the barrel.

In the United States the 3-inch Ordnance rifles of Civil War fame (see pages 22-23) remained standard until almost 1900 – though new 3·2-inch breech-loading rifles were used in the Spanish-American War (1898). In this respect the United States was the most conservative of the Great Powers – a state of mind induced by her more or less isolated position. For her there was simply no compelling reason to modernize or re-equip.

The Russo-Turkish War (1877–78) was in many ways a very modern war. It was the first in which the infantry was uniformly equipped with modern repeating rifles and in which the field artillery of both sides used only breech-loading rifles. The Krupp Works had equipped the artillery park of Sultan Abdul Azeez with 4- and 6-pounder steel breech-loaders, developed after the Battle of Königgrätz (1866), while the Czar had dropped his 'Napoleon' muzzle-loaders after 1870 and re-equipped with Krupp bronze 4- and 9-pounders. Both nations evidently liked what they were buying, for throughout the latter half of the 19th century Russia and Turkey were Krupp's biggest foreign customers.

LEFT *Count von Schlieffen, German Chief of Staff 1891–1906, whose master plan for a European war hinged on the invasion of France through Belgium. To deal with the barrier posed by the Belgian forts, Krupp developed their giant 42-cm howitzers.*

This was also the first European war in which improvised field-works were commonplace, the Russians being especially skilled in this area. Against them the artillery formed the crack arm of the Sultan's forces.

Despite their modern equipment, artillerymen still preferred in those days to fight their guns on the infantry line. This tendency to close to short range had been observable in all the wars of this era, and may be attributed more to the lack of modern sights and powerful explosive shells than to other factors. Until these problems were solved, artillerists could not exploit the improved ranges and rapid-firing qualities of their guns to proper effect.

In 1883 the German General Kolmar von der Goltz wrote that 'each new invention and each mechanical improvement seems, somehow, in these days, to find its way into military service'. Ordnance benefited particularly from the great outpouring of scientific ideas, and within a very short time it had been completely transformed.

This rush of scientific activity was on the whole carried out in a humanitarian spirit. Von der Goltz himself believed that science and invention would make wars shorter, perhaps end war altogether; in this he echoed the notion of Robert Southey, the English poet, that 'the chemist and the mechanist will succeed where moralists and divines have failed'. Few foresaw that these developments would make possible the unprecedented carnage of World War I.

The barrel of the 28-cm howitzer joins up with the carriage. The caterpillars or pattens on the wheels helped to distribute the gun's weight and improved stability.

Some of the most important of the new developments were:

1 Improved time fuses were devised in France *c*. 1877.
2 The first good smokeless powder was developed by a Frenchman, Paul Vieille, in 1884; the powder was called 'Poudre B' after General Boulanger. In 1891 the British first produced cordite, a smokeless powder that was stable and retained its potency over a long period of time. Flashless powder (which did nevertheless produce smoke) was developed for night firing during World War I.
3 In 1888 Konrad Haussner developed the revolutionary long-recoil cylinder, which made possible Quick-Firing (QF) guns.
4 By 1896 wire-wound heavy guns were being constructed. These guns were superior by far to the comparatively brittle cast or forged guns. Subsequently frettage, a system in which hot steel tubes were shrunk onto one another, became the chief method of constructing guns.
5 The QF field-gun demanded 'fixed' ammunition, and during this period first brass and then steel cartridges were produced. ('Fixed' ammunition employs one cartridge-type unit for both charge and projectile, unlike 'bag' ammunition in which the projectile and bag charge are loaded separately.)

The impressive performance of rifled siege guns had rendered every existing brick fort obsolete. European nations sought, therefore, to rebuild their frontier defences using new ideas. The French system, designed by General Séré de Rivière, was begun in 1873. It consisted of fortified localities defended by detached forts. The forts were built of concrete covered with earth, they had cast-steel gun turrets and subterranean magazines and living quarters, and each was meant to be self-sufficient in defence.

The fear of invasion would, in time, lead other nations to construct similar defensive systems. The Germans began a network of forts along the line Thionville-Metz-Strasbourg and then along the Rhine to the Swiss border at Basle. Eventually the Russians and Rumanians began fortress systems, and in 1888 the Belgian engineer Brialmont began the construction of forts at Liège, Namur and other Belgian towns. The Belgian system then complemented and extended the French system northwards.

All this construction was to have an effect on ordnance. The sizes of fortresses and manageable siege guns increased tremendously in the late 19th century. Krupp produced howitzers of 21-cm calibre for the German Foot Artillery. Additionally *die Firma*, as the Krupp Works was also known, embarked on an ambitious programme of its own for a 42-cm howitzer.

Krupp's first 42-cm type, known as the 'heavy Gamma implement', was demonstrated to the German General Staff in 1911. As it happened, these guns were just what the General Staff thought necessary to deal with Brialmont's forts. Under the German contingency plan for a European war (called the Schlieffen Plan after Count von Schlieffen, Chief of the General Staff, 1891–1906) the German armies were to swing north through a neutral Belgium (thereby avoiding de Rivière's forts) and descend from the northeast onto the flank of the French armies guarding the frontier. The Belgian forts would block the flow of this movement, but it was thought that Krupp's monster 42-cm howitzers would be able to deal with them.

The only problem remaining was that of mobility. The 'Gamma implements' which were first produced had to be transported by rail and required a heavy-duty concrete emplacement before they could be brought into action. While all this was happening, of course, the French armies would be able to re-deploy to meet the thrust of the Schlieffen operation.

RIGHT *Cross-section of a steel observation turret set in concrete, devised by the fortress-minded firm of Grusonwerk.*
BELOW *The proving ground of Bofors, the Swedish firm, in 1913. The gap in the tree-line allowed for low-trajectory gunfire.*
BELOW RIGHT *Another German invention of the period was Gruson's 12-cm spherical mortar, seen with its accessories.*

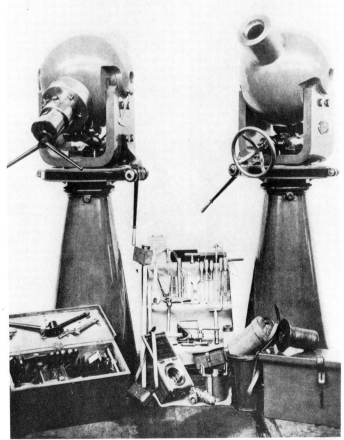

Krupp solved this problem by creating a lighter 42-cm howitzer which became known as the 'M-implement', or more familiarly as 'Big Bertha'. The new weapon had a shorter barrel than the General Staff's railway gun and was broken down into four loads for road transport. There was, furthermore, no need to construct a special emplacement to bring the gun into action. When the M-implement was fired, its 1,800-pound shell rose almost vertically for three miles and then began to plunge at a very high velocity onto the target some 10,000 yards away. The effect of such a shell may well be imagined.

The Spanish-American War (1898) and the Boer War (1899–1902), although separated in time by barely a year, might well have been decades apart in artillery technique. The US gunners in Cuba used the 3·2-inch breech-loading rifle introduced for service in 1893, and later described by one artilleryman as 'the latest, and the last development of the old non-recoil material, firing unfixed ammunition with black powder charges and unprovided with any kind of laying apparatus for indirect fire'. Against them Spanish sharpshooters firing Mauser magazine rifles forced the gunners to stay beyond an effective range (2,600 yards at El Pozo, for example) for guns equipped with primitive sights, and American artillery fire was ineffectual. By far the most useful guns in the campaign were machine guns like the Hotchkiss 1-pounder revolving cannon.

In the Boer War the British faced similar problems. Their gunners were well equipped with rapid-fire rifled breech-loaders: field artillery batteries used a 15-pounder, field howitzer batteries a 5-inch howitzer and the Royal Horse Artillery a 12-pounder. These guns were not in the same class as the modern French and German guns of the Boer artillery, but the Boers never fielded more than a handful of guns at any one time. The real problem for the British was

ABOVE *A 3·2-inch breech-loading rifle, standard US field gun in the Spanish-American War and in the Philippines.*
BELOW *The dynamite gun attached to the Rough Riders cavalry regiment, seen in the trenches on San Juan Hill, Cuba, 1888.*
OPPOSITE *A Spanish 12-inch coastal defence gun of the Santa Clara Battery at Vedado, Cuba.*

the Boer mounted rifleman. Equipped with Mausers, like the Spanish in Cuba, these men were expert shots and adept at picking off gunners from a distance. In their response, however, the British artillerymen were more successful than their US counterparts. They learned the technique of indirect fire and also to utilize every scrap of cover and dip of ground in the sparse veldt. The Boer War was in fact the first war in which indirect fire and firing from concealed positions were extensively used.

One oddity made its début in Cuba during the Spanish-American War. This was the dynamite field gun invented by Captain E.L. Zalinsky, an American engineer. These guns were basically terror weapons, incapable of doing much damage to infantry in open order, since they depended for their effect on the blast of their dynamite and gelatine charge rather than on splinters. The gun used in Cuba was attached to the Rough Riders cavalry regiment and was fired into Santiago from the trenches on San Juan Hill.

In order to fire a material as unstable as dynamite with relative safety, Zalinsky utilized a combustion chamber separate from the firing tube. Approximately 7–9 ounces of smokeless powder were detonated in the combustion chamber, compressing the air in the chamber. The compressed air was then conducted into the firing tube behind the shell casing, forcing it along the barrel. The gun had a range of 2,600–3,600 yards depending on the amount of combustion powder used: it was not much used in the war because of its short range and inaccuracy.

The Boer War was also notable for freak guns. Prominent among them were the 'home-made' guns used to help defend the towns of Mafeking and Kimberley. The 'Wolf', a 4·5-inch howitzer used at Mafeking, had a barrel made from a drainpipe. 'Long Cecil', the Kimberley gun, was more conventional but was made in the factory of a mining company by men who had never made a gun before.

Immediately following the Spanish-American War, United States troops became involved in putting down the insurrection of Emilio Aguinaldo in the Philippines. This difficult guerrilla war, fought largely in paddy and bamboo jungle, cost the US Army more men than the Spanish-American War. A few guns were available but not much ammunition. Even so, the field guns were next to useless against the *insurrectos*, who took care to construct wide-ranging systems of slit trenches whenever they decided to defend a locality. One US artilleryman, commenting on the difficulty of shelling the rudimentary works of the Filipinos, repeated the old adage that 'you cannot shoot an enemy out of a position'. The plain fact was that the modern shrapnel shell, so recently invented, was proving to be useless against troops clever enough to conceal themselves; nor could field guns designed for low-trajectory work fire their HE with any real effect against trenches.

In the Russo-Japanese War (1904–5) indirect fire was the norm. Improved panoramic sights, goniometers (for measuring angles), aerial observation (by balloon) and the extensive use of field telephones, especially by the Japanese, allowed batteries to fire on targets they could not see but which were within their range. Since a gun's field of fire was now equal to the frontage of an army corps, flag and telephone communication sufficed to bring the entire weight of a corp's artillery onto a target.

OPPOSITE, TOP *A British howitzer battery in the Boer War; the gun shown is a 5-inch field howitzer, introduced in 1896.*
LEFT *Royal Artillery gun crew at the ready in South Africa.*
THIS PAGE, TOP *'Home-made' artillery piece at Mafeking, 1899.*
ABOVE *British 4·7-inch high-velocity naval guns of HMS* Monarch *and* Dora *on the road to Bloemfontein. The gunners have lightened their personal loads by draping various items of kit over the barrels of the guns.*

At the beginning of the war the Russian field artillery received a new long-recoil type Quick-Firing field gun – the M-1903 Putilov 76·2-mm. This gun, an improvement on a similar 1900 model, was very modern; even so it was heavier and less mobile than the comparable Japanese gun. (The older M-1900 76·2-mm gun had, incidentally, an interesting and unique feature – a recoil system made of India rubber to avoid freezing in the severe Manchurian winter.)

The standard Japanese field gun was designated the 7-cm (actual calibre 7·5-cm) M-31 (1898). This gun did not have a modern recoil system and its overall performance was unsatisfactory; nevertheless its light weight was a distinct advantage in the trackless wastes of Manchuria. Its replacement, the Type 38 (1905) 75-mm gun, was not produced in time to see action in the war, but incorporated design features that the Japanese felt essential after their experiences with the Type 31. It had a hydraulic buffer system, improved sights and increased velocity. The Type 38 remained in service until World War II. It is interesting also to note here that the Japanese had used French

4-pounders up to the time of the Franco-Prussian War, and Krupp rifles thereafter. The first field guns manufactured in Japan were 4-pounder muzzle-loaders produced at the Osaka arsenal in 1872.

One of the more modern aspects of the Russo-Japanese War was the need for batteries to conceal their positions from enemy observers. The Japanese brought the art of camouflage to a high state during the war, using trees and netting to hide their guns and even watering trails along which guns were to be moved so that their movement would not raise tell-tale clouds of dust.

The six-month siege of Port Arthur by the Japanese was a turning-point in the war. General Velichko, the man who planned the Port Arthur defences, was a highly competent engineer with advanced ideas. While he did not totally reject the ideas of Brialmont and de Rivière, he did not accept their contention that all the guns in a perimeter defence must be in the forts. The forts that Velichko designed for Port Arthur contained a few heavy guns, but most of the guns were outside the forts in batteries. This meant that the attacker would have to divide his fire, also that there would be no 'dead' ground which might allow his infantry to slip through the perimeter unmolested by artillery fire.

The Japanese attacked Velichko's forts using the heaviest ordnance and most up-to-date fire-direction and ranging

OPPOSITE *US 1·65-inch infantry cannon in the Philippines.*
ABOVE *US light artillery at Naco, Mexico, in 1915. In the right foreground is a Gatling 1-pounder heavy machine gun. To the left and rear are M-1903 3-inch cannon.*
BELOW *Krupp 15-cm breech-loading rifles captured by the Allied Expeditionary Force during the Boxer Rebellion, 1900.*

equipment then available. Before this siege 15-cm guns and howitzers, such as the Prussians had used against Paris in 1871, had been the largest pieces normally found in siege trains. At Port Arthur the Japanese used howitzers up to 28-cm in calibre.

The Japanese artillery command post was sophisticated even by later standards. A camera obscura was used to study the Russian fortifications in the manner of a periscope, and

ABOVE *Japanese artillery officers observe the effect of the fire of their mountain guns during the Russo-Japanese War.*

BELOW *Breech-loading rifles in a Russian fort overlooking the harbour of Port Arthur.*

OPPOSITE. *In the upper picture a Japanese field gun is manhandled into position under fire. Below is a heavy gun at Port Arthur, 1905. Note the obsolescent barbette carriage and observation tower at left – equipment typical of that supplied to imperial outposts at the turn of the century.*

telephone lines relayed the orders of the chief of artillery to each battery. Even when the artillery commander left his concrete command post, he was followed by a man playing out telephone cable so that he should be in instantaneous communication with his batteries at any time.

Despite their thorough organization, the initial effect of the Japanese bombardment was less than decisive. Eventually, however, a crucial Russian fortress (203-Metre Hill) was taken with heavy infantry losses. That was the moment of breakthrough. For when the Japanese then emplaced 28-cm howitzers on 203-Metre Hill and bombarded the Russian Pacific fleet in the harbour 4,000 yards away, only one vessel, the *Sebastopol* (ironically enough), escaped scuttling or sinking. It was the beginning of the end; within a few weeks the survivors in the Russian garrison surrendered.

The Artillery War 1914–1918
A Chronology

THE SYMBOL ☐ DENOTES ACTIVITY OVER A PERIOD OF TIME

1914

AUGUST

1 Germany declares war on Russia, followed on 6th by Austria-Hungary.

3 Germany declares war on France and invades Belgium.

4 Britain declares war on Germany. Liège forts surrender after bombardment by Krupp 42-cm 'Berthas'.

20 Fall of Brussels.

20-25 Main German force sweeps back Allies at Battles of Mons, the Sambre and the Ardennes.

25 Namur forts surrender after bombardment by 'Berthas' and 30·5-cm 'Emmas'.

SEPTEMBER

5-10 First Battle of the Marne. Puteaux '75s' instrumental in French victory. Germans withdraw to a line Noyon-Verdun.

15-18 First Battle of the Aisne. Armies swing northwards to coast.

OCTOBER–NOVEMBER

☐ Heavy fighting in Flanders. British Expeditionary Force denies Channel ports to German Army in First Battle of Ypres (30 October–24 November).

NOVEMBER

1 Allies declare war on Turkey.

DECEMBER

☐ Germans dig in along Western Front, establishing static trench warfare from North Sea, near Nieuport, to Swiss border near Belfort.

1915

JANUARY–JUNE

☐ Allied offensives on Western Front beaten back.

FEBRUARY

15 First naval assault at Dardanelles.

18 Opening of first submarine campaign against Allied commerce.

MARCH

10 Battle of Neuve Chapelle. First great artillery barrage of war fired as preparation for British attack.

22 Surrender to Russians of Przemsyl, Bohemian fortress, after heavy bombardment and siege lasting 194 days.

APRIL

22 First use of gas–by Germans at Second Battle of Ypres.

25 British landings at Gallipoli.

☐ German build-up on Eastern Front.

MAY

2 Austro-German armies break through at Gorlice-Tarnow after four-hour bombardment. Italy declares war on Austria-Hungary.

JUNE–SEPTEMBER

☐ Russians retreat to line south of Riga.

SEPTEMBER–NOVEMBER

☐ Allies renew offensive on Western Front with small success.

1916

JANUARY

9 Evacuation completed after unsuccessful Dardanelles Expedition.

FEBRUARY

21 Siege of Verdun begins after intensive four-hour bombardment by massed German guns.

JUNE

24 First Battle of the Somme opens with seven-day artillery assault by Allies.

JUNE–SEPTEMBER

☐ New Russian offensive under General Brusilov weakens resources of Central Powers, notably at Verdun and in Italy.

SEPTEMBER

15 Tanks make first appearance in final phase of Battle of the Somme.

1917

FEBRUARY

1 Germans launch unrestricted submarine warfare against commerce.

FEBRUARY–APRIL

☐ Germans withdraw to heavily defended zone–the Hindenburg Line.

MARCH

12 Start of First Russian Revolution.

APRIL

6 USA declares war on Germany.

9-15 Battle of Arras. British attack in preparation for Nivelle Offensive.

16-20 Nivelle Offensive. Disastrous attack by 1·2 million French backed by 7,000 guns.

JUNE

7 Battle of Messines. British attack after 17-day bombardment consuming 3·5 million shells.

☐ First division of American Expeditionary Force shipped to France.

JULY–NOVEMBER

☐ Third Battle of Ypres (Passchendaele). Preliminary bombardment of 4·3 million shells; altogether 107,000 tons of shells fired in greatest artillery concentration in British history.

SEPTEMBER

1 General von Hutier's Riga Offensive begins after short intensive bombardment planned by Colonel Bruchmüller.

OCTOBER–NOVEMBER

☐ Battle of Caporetto. Germans and Austrians use 'Hutier' tactics to break through on Italian Front.

NOVEMBER

7 Second Russian Revolution. Lenin and Trotsky seize power.

20 British Mark IV tanks used en masse at Battle of Cambrai to force extensive breach in Hindenburg Line.

DECEMBER

15 Russia and Germany agree armistice terms.

1918

MARCH

21 Ludendorff opens spring offensives on Western Front. German stormtroopers attack after five-hour bombardment.

23 Paris Gun opens fire; on 29th, Good Friday, shell collapses vault of Church of St Gervais, near Hôtel de Ville, killing 88 worshippers. Shelling continues intermittently until 7 August.

APRIL

9-17 Ludendorff's second offensive (Luys).

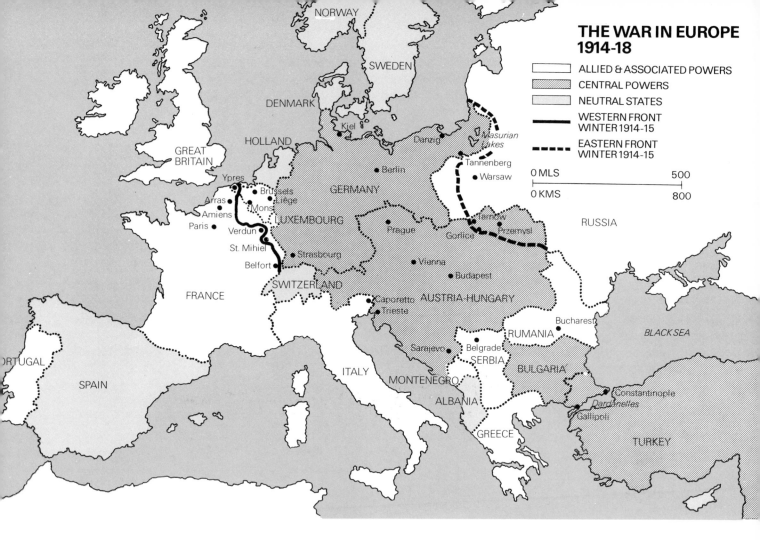

ALLIED & ASSOCIATED POWERS
CENTRAL POWERS
NEUTRAL STATES
WESTERN FRONT WINTER 1914-15
EASTERN FRONT WINTER 1914-15

0 MLS   500
0 KMS   800

MAY

27   Ludendorff's third offensive (Aisne) begins; lasts until 17 June.

28   Battle of Cantigny marks first American offensive in this war; followed on 30th by Battles of Château-Thierry and Belleau Wood.

JUNE

9–13   Ludendorff's fourth offensive (Noyon-Montdidier). Assault of Hutier's 18th Army disrupted by Allied counter-preparation bombardment.

JULY

5–19   Ludendorff's fifth offensive (Champagne-Meuse). Allied counter-preparation bombardment again breaks up German stormtrooper formations.
Allied counter-offensive begins on Aisne-Marne front.

AUGUST

8   'Black Day' of German Army: Allies advance seven miles in nine hours at Battle of Amiens.

SEPTEMBER

12–16   American ground and combined ground-air assaults drive Germans out of St Mihiel salient.

26   Americans begin Meuse-Argonne offensive.

27   British begin storming of Hindenburg Line.

28   Allied offensive opens in Flanders.

OCTOBER

6   First German request for armistice.

27   Ludendorff resigns. Austria-Hungary sues for armistice.

29   Mutiny at Kiel of German High Seas Fleet.

31   Revolution in Vienna and Budapest.

NOVEMBER

9   Revolution in Berlin.

10   Flight of Kaiser.

11   Armistice concluded with Germany.

Captured French heavy mortars in their emplacements, June 1918.

Chapter Three
World War I

In the years leading up to 1914 few Allied strategists accurately foresaw how increased firepower would influence the course of the next war. The French and the British prepared for a war of movement in which the decisive actions would be fought along classical lines and the enemy defeated after a short campaign. In such a war heavy artillery and machine guns (seen as static or defensive weapons) would not be important factors, and the French and British general staffs reduced the number of such weapons in their tables of organization.

The Germans, as it turned out, planned more wisely. They placed their faith in the weight of fire available to each division and army corps. They did not go along with the idea, then current in France, that the hypothetical battlefield of the future would be dominated by light Quick-Firers like the '75'; they had, moreover, the foresight to integrate numbers of light howitzers with their divisional artillery, and they also provided heavy howitzers at corps level.

Broadly, by 1914 the tactical doctrine of the major fighting nations may be summarized as follows:

RIGHT *In the two lower pictures 'Granny', one of the British Admiralty's 15-inch heavy howitzers, is loaded and fired. Painted on the side of the gun are the names of actions in which it has fought ... Aubers Ridge, Festubert, Loos, Ypres.*

ABOVE *British 9·2-inch heavy howitzers are seen in battery on the Western Front; in the foreground a supply of shells is lined up on a ramp. To the rear of the battery passes an ammunition column whose function is to feed the lighter guns closer to the front line.*
OPPOSITE *The efficient Russian 76·2-mm field gun M-1903.*

IMPROVEMENT OF FIELD GUNS 1815–1919

CATEGORY	TYPE OF GUN	DATE	PERFORMANCE
1 Muzzle velocity	Early rifled guns	1863–70	1,090 feet per second
	Later rifled guns	1870–93	1,466 feet per second
	Early Quick-Firers	c. 1900	1,696 feet per second
	Later Quick-Firers	1914–18	1,770 feet per second
2 Range with shrapnel	Smooth-bores	1815–50	1,257 yards
	Early rifled guns	1863–70	2,004 yards
	Later rifled guns	1870–93	4,120 yards
	Early Quick-Firers	c. 1900	6,160 yards
	Later Quick-Firers	1914–18	6,500 yards
3 Range with shell	Smooth-bores	1815–50	1,670 yards
	Early rifled guns	1863–70	3,965 yards
	Later rifled guns	1870–93	6,168 yards
	Early Quick-Firers	c. 1900	7,340 yards
	Later Quick-Firers	1914–18	8,500 yards
	With streamline shell	1918–19	12,130 yards

1 ALLIES

France. French tactical use of artillery in 1914 was centred entirely on the M-1897 Puteaux 75-mm field-gun. The '75', although a superior direct-fire weapon, was tactically obsolete in 1914 because its low-trajectory fire was ineffective against infantry or artillery sheltering behind rudimentary field works or in convolutions of the terrain. In such situations the howitzer, with its mid-angle trajectory, was at its best, but for various reasons the French were woefully deficient in howitzers.

In the event of the French meeting an enemy in the open, a group of three 4-gun batteries (amounting to one-third of the '75s' attached to each division) would act as 'infantry batteries', firing on the objectives of the *poilus* (as the French infantrymen were known). The rest of the divisional artillery engaged the enemy's guns.

The French exaggerated the counter-battery potential of the '75' and, again, visions of batteries going into action at a smart trot, fighting in the open from 'semi-concealed' positions and engaging and defeating opportunity targets danced in the minds of senior officers. It was as if the next war would duplicate the conditions of 1870. This time, though, the French saw themselves wielding the stick, and in the aura of confidence surrounding 'notre glorieux "soixante-quinze"' ('our glorious "75"'), the gun's limitations went unnoticed and some of the technical improvements of the previous decade – such as telephone communication between groups of batteries – were ignored.

Great Britain. British tactical use of artillery and organization closely resembled German practice (see below), but the British howitzers were obsolete in 1914 and, besides, were often supplied with defective ammunition. Also, the British were deficient in weight of metal and numbers of guns at army corps level. Standard British field-pieces included the 3·3-inch 18-pounder and the 4·5-inch howitzer. Heavy fire was provided by the 5-inch 60-pounder, which in 1914 had a range of 10,500 yards.

Russia. The artillery was the crack arm of the Czar's Army. The Putilov 76·2-mm field-gun was comparable to anything the Germans or Austrians could field, but the Russians were without a good field or heavy howitzer. Numbers of elderly Krupp howitzers and 155-mm 'long' guns were available, but these guns were not up to 1914 standards. A Russian copy of the Schneider 155-mm howitzer was produced but not in quantity, and the Czar's artillery, caught in the middle of a modernization programme, never was able to recover from its handicap in this category.

French 75-mm Puteaux Field Gun M-1897

The '75' was the first modern Quick-Firing field gun. Its appearance in 1897 heralded a revolution in the design and capabilities of artillery. The 'secret' of the 75-mm gun and the mechanism that set it apart from all previous guns was its long recoil cylinder – a device which absorbed the energy of the recoil and returned the gun to battery smoothly and efficiently without disturbing the position of the gun's carriage. This removed the need to re-lay the gun after each shot (a time-consuming operation) and made possible a high rate of fire.

The '75' was the invention of Commandant de Port of the Ateliers de Puteaux. By 1898 the first guns were in service. Subsequently the gun went on campaign in China, Morocco and the Balkan Wars. During World War I the '75' was the standard field gun of France and the American Expeditionary Force; many were still in service in World War II.

Operation of the Nordenfeldt eccentric screw breech block

The mechanism was opened by grasping the handle and turning the breech block 120 degrees to the left. This circular displacement uncovered the bore. A cartridge was inserted into the breech, and a reverse motion closed the breech block. These very simple motions could be performed by a skilled crew in a few seconds. Obturation, *i.e.* the sealing of the breech to prevent the escape of gases, was performed by the metallic cartridge case.

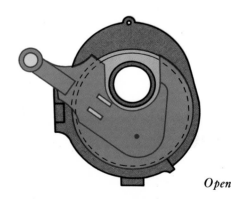

Open

LEFT *Two shell types fired by the '75'. The upper diagram features the 12-pound HE (high explosive) shell which was filled with melanite. In the lower picture is the heavier 16-pound shrapnel shell.*

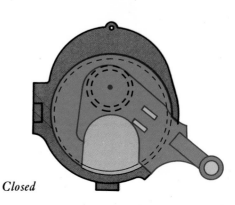

Closed

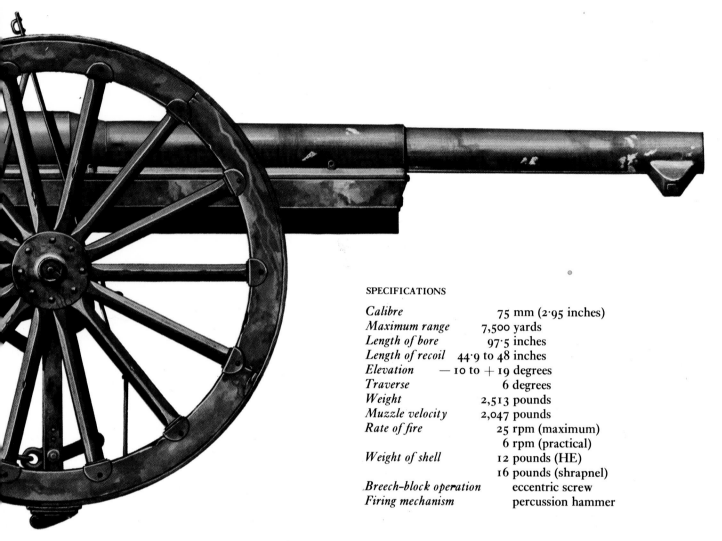

SPECIFICATIONS

Calibre	75 mm (2·95 inches)
Maximum range	7,500 yards
Length of bore	97·5 inches
Length of recoil	44·9 to 48 inches
Elevation	— 10 to + 19 degrees
Traverse	6 degrees
Weight	2,513 pounds
Muzzle velocity	2,047 pounds
Rate of fire	25 rpm (maximum)
	6 rpm (practical)
Weight of shell	12 pounds (HE)
	16 pounds (shrapnel)
Breech-block operation	eccentric screw
Firing mechanism	percussion hammer

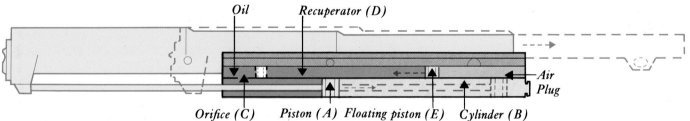

Oil   Recuperator (D)

Orifice (C)   Piston (A) Floating piston (E) Cylinder (B)

Air Plug

Operation of the long-recoil cylinder

When the gun is fired, the piston (A) is drawn through a cylinder (B) filled with oil. The action of the piston compresses the oil and forces it through a small orifice (C) into another cylinder, the recuperator (D), which is filled with compressed air beyond the floating piston (E). The energy of the recoil then further compresses the air in the recuperator until, the recoil force being dissipated, the compressed air 'spring' forces the oil back into the recoil cylinder and returns the gun to battery.

The long-recoil cylinder was the invention of Konrad Haussner, a Krupp engineer, but it was rejected by Krupp and the German authorities as 'impracticable for use in the field'. There can be no doubt that the French worked directly from Haussner's patent in designing their long-recoil cylinder for the '75'.

LEFT *The caisson or ammunition chest in which shells for the '75' were towed to the firing position.*

2 CENTRAL POWERS

Germany. The Germans not only had a reliable field-gun in the much-reworked Krupp 77-mm M-1906, they also recognized the inherent limitations of field guns, and so they provided three batteries of light 105-mm howitzers for every nine of field guns at division level. Backing these were heavier 155-mm howitzers at corps level. In addition there was an extraordinary number of heavier howitzers and field mortars (all of which were remarkably mobile) in the heavy batteries of the Foot Artillery.

The Germans made extensive use of indirect fire in their pre-war manoeuvres and were rarely seen in the open, preferring to fight from carefully chosen, fully concealed positions. The *Abteilung* system (effectively a three-battery group) was still in use, and, as in 1870, artillery took precedence over infantry in positioning.

The first great artillery event of the war was not announced by the drum-fire of the '75s' but rather by the earth-shaking roar of Krupp's monster 42-cm Berthas bombarding the Belgian forts. So much nonsense has been written about this event that it sometimes becomes difficult to sift fact from fancy, or, worse yet, to separate the truth from the 'big lie'. There can be no doubt that the propaganda mills were churning at a great rate after the bombardment; oddly enough, too, the story they told suited everyone's purpose. Certainly, the reputation of the Big Berthas seems to rest solely on their performance against the Belgian forts, for when the same guns were used against Ypres in April 1915, and later against Verdun, they produced nothing more than a great deal of noise and much German disappointment.

The generally accepted account of the bombardment is that, in accordance with the Schlieffen Plan, the German Army of the Meuse under General von Emmich swung through neutral Belgium with the object of enveloping the Allied left flank. On 3 August 1914 the German army entered Belgian territory, and by 4 August the Germans faced their first serious obstacle, the Brialmont forts at Liège. German infantry failed to take the forts but filtered through the 'dead spaces' in the perimeter and captured the town of Liège four miles beyond. However, the forts had to be taken before the invasion could proceed.

There were two Berthas with von Emmich's army. By 12 August the laborious task of emplacing them had been completed, and early that evening they began the systematic reduction of each fort. According to the Belgian commander, General Léman, the guns' shells tore holes in the ground large enough to 'put a three-storey house in'. The morale of the defenders cracked under the terrible bombardment. The forts were wrecked one by one. The concrete was penetrated time and again, steel gun turrets were blown topsy-turvy and the survivors of each garrison emerged dumbly amid the rubble and smoke.

After reducing the eastern perimeter, the Berthas were shifted into the town itself and began to pound the western forts. General Léman was pulled dazed from the ruins of Fort Loncin after a shell penetrated its concrete and blew up the magazine. By 16 August the Belgians had had enough, and the last forts surrendered. The two Berthas had caused the surrender of each fort – some through devastating bombardment and others through intimidation.

From Liège the Berthas moved to Namur where they were joined by a two-gun battery of Austro-Hungarian 30·5-cm 'Schlanke (slim) Emmas'. The Brialmont forts at Namur surrendered after a four-day bombardment (21–25 August 1914) by the four howitzers. After Namur the forts at Maubeuge were subjected to the same treatment.

If we accept this version of events, two Berthas and four Emmas (a second Emma battery was present at Maubeuge) battered a path for the German Army through three obsolete but quite formidable fortress systems. In this context the German 'secret weapon' (as its propagandists called it) was a great success. Meanwhile, too, the Allies could claim that the gallant resistance of the tiny Belgian Army in the face of these 'terror weapons' (their term for the Berthas) gained precious time for the French and the British Expeditionary Force to complete their mobilization and deployment; this in turn helped to produce victory at the First Battle of the Marne.

On the other hand, it becomes difficult to suppress doubts about the veracity of official German and Belgian accounts after reading Lt-Col Karl Justrow's narrative in *Die Dicke Berta und der Krieg*. According to Justrow, who was in a position to know, those tremendous holes Léman spoke of were not caused by the Berthas but, rather, were the result of dynamiting by German engineers after the surrender.

OPPOSITE *A German 77-mm field gun C 96 n/A firing in the Champagne sector of the Western Front.*
ABOVE *German gunners on winter watch in the Vosges Mountains; the gun is a 155-mm heavy howitzer.*
BELOW *Firmly emplaced in the post-1914 deadlock—a German 105-mm light howitzer 98/09.*

von EMMICH

One begins in fact to suspect that the photographers were assembled *after* the dynamiting so that more impressive pictures could be taken of the 'devastation' wrought by the Berthas.

In addition, there is testimony here and there in German reports that the bombardment produced, in the words of one account, 'a *superficial* picture of indescribable devastation, with heaps of earth and debris everywhere' (my italics). This, coupled with the comparatively slight losses of the Belgian garrisons, seems to point to the fact that the Belgians simply lost their nerve and surrendered to a lot of noise, smoke and dust. Finally, there is the unquestionable failure of the Berthas after the Belgian campaign. It seems, for example, that in the operations against Verdun Bertha's shells could not penetrate concrete and shattered upon striking the steel turrets of the forts. But whichever version of the Belgian campaign one believes, there is no doubt that the Berthas made a lasting contribution to the folklore of war–even if their period of supremacy was limited to a few days in August 1914.

The German invasion was brought to a halt little more than 20 miles from Paris in the mammoth First Battle of the Marne (5–10 September 1914). French armies under Marshal Joffre and General Galliéni checked the advance of General von Gronau's right-flank forces on 6 September, and by 8 September the Germans had begun to retreat to the Aisne. The French 75-mm guns, operating in the open for the last time until the 1916 breakthrough battles, seemed to be everywhere. They savaged the German infantry advance with rapid fire *rafales*–storms of shells that could blanket and obliterate an infantry column in seconds. On some occasions, as happened for instance at the Grand Couronné de Nancy, the fire of the '75s' alone was sufficient to break up major German attacks.

The German artillery, on the other hand, fired very effectively from concealment. It soon became apparent too that, despite its effectiveness against infantry in the open, the '75' was failing in the counter-battery role. Losses in the '75' batteries were very high, not least because of the inanely rough-and-ready tactics of the French gunners, who on countless occasions exposed themselves needlessly to German fire. Moreover, the German heavy howitzers never failed to capitalize on their advantage in range over the heaviest French guns. Victory at the Marne was bought not so much by the '75s' as by a tremendous sacrifice of

OPPOSITE *A German 77-mm field-gun crew dashes forward under fire at the Marne; from a painting by Albert Reich. Inset is General von Emmich, whose Army of the Meuse invaded Belgium with two 42-cm Berthas, pride of the Krupp works.*
ABOVE RIGHT *A Big Bertha and crew; despite their awesome size, the supremacy of these super-guns was essentially limited to the first weeks of the war.*
RIGHT *A German war artist's impression of a heavy gun in position beside the Weichsel River in Poland.*

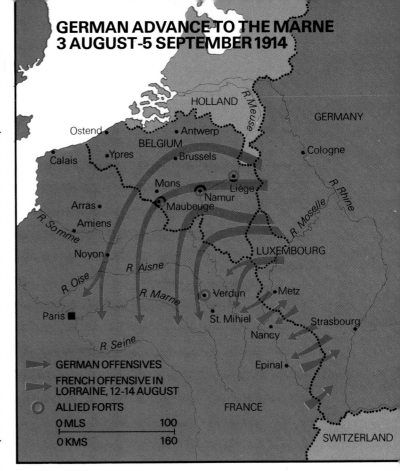

GERMAN ADVANCE TO THE MARNE
3 AUGUST-5 SEPTEMBER 1914

HOLLAND
GERMANY
Ostend • Antwerp
BELGIUM • Cologne
Calais • Ypres • Brussels
Mons • Liège
Arras • Namur
Maubeuge
Amiens LUXEMBOURG
Noyon
R. Aisne
R. Oise • Verdun • Metz
R. Marne St. Mihiel
Paris ■ Strasbourg
Nancy
R. Seine
Epinal
GERMAN OFFENSIVES FRANCE
FRENCH OFFENSIVE IN
LORRAINE, 12-14 AUGUST
○ ALLIED FORTS
0 MLS 100
0 KMS 160 SWITZERLAND

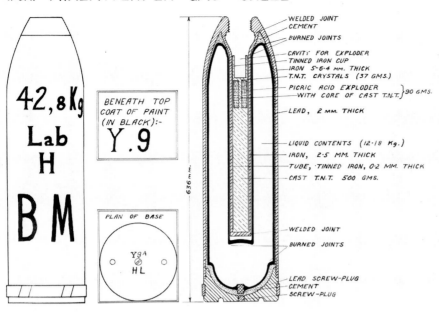

17cm. MINENWERFER GAS SHELL

42,8 Kg
Lab
H
B M

BENEATH TOP
COAT OF PAINT
(IN BLACK):-
Y.9

PLAN OF BASE

Y9ᴬ
HL

636 mm.

WELDED JOINT
CEMENT
BURNED JOINTS
CAVITY FOR EXPLODER
TINNED IRON CUP
IRON 5·6·4 MM. THICK
T.N.T. CRYSTALS (37 GMS.)
PICRIC ACID EXPLODER
WITH CORE OF CAST T.N.T. } 90 GMS.
LEAD, 2 MM. THICK

LIQUID CONTENTS (12·18 Kg.)
IRON, 2·5 MM. THICK
TUBE, TINNED IRON, 0·2 MM. THICK
CAST T.N.T. 500 GMS.

WELDED JOINT
BURNED JOINTS

LEAD SCREW-PLUG
CEMENT
SCREW-PLUG

ABOVE *Cross-section of a German terror weapon—the gas shell delivered by the 170-mm medium Minenwerfer. The latter had a range of 1,100 yards.*
BELOW *On the Isonzo Front men of the Austrian 16th Corps go through the motions of loading a 220-mm Minenwerfer.*

TYPES OF GERMAN TRENCH MORTAR IN WORLD WAR I

TYPE	CALIBRE	WEIGHT (POUNDS)	RANGE (YARDS)
Early light rifle	3 inches	220	1,150
Improved light rifle	3 inches	312	1,420
Medium	170 mm (6·7 inches)	1,100	1,100
Smooth-bore Minenwerfer	180 mm (7 inches)	1,000	550
Flugelminenwerfer	240 mm (9·45 inches)	3,000	1,700
'Albrecht'	—	3,500	2,200
Heavy rifled muzzle-loader	245 mm (9·8 inches)	1,362	600 (with light Drake projectile) 1,000 (with heavy shell)

OPPOSITE *In the trenches a German artillery officer uses a stereoscopic telescope to observe the effect of gunfire.* BELOW *A cross-section of the Allied Livens gas projector, usually fired in deadly banks of 25.*

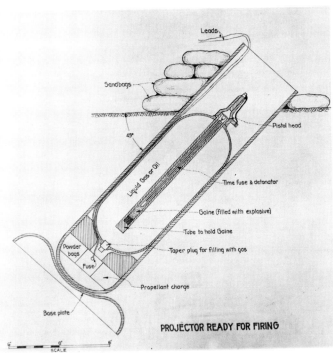

PROJECTOR READY FOR FIRING

lives. French losses in August–September 1914 totalled 329,000 men, fully one-sixth of their total for the war.

After the Marne the war on the Western Front degenerated into a stalemate. Both sides rapidly constructed parallel lines of trenches from Nieuport on the English Channel to the Swiss frontier 450 miles away. For the first time in history armies fought a war in which there were no flanks; victory could be gained only by costly frontal attacks

or by exhausting the enemy's ability or will to make war. On the Eastern Front a similar situation prevailed following the early German victories at Tannenberg and the Masurian Lakes. Later on, new fronts were established in northern Italy and the Balkans.

The Germans were well prepared for this new form of warfare. In addition to their large stocks of machine guns and heavy artillery, they possessed 2,000 trench mortars, or Minenwerfer. The trench mortar was not new—great numbers of them had been used in the American Civil War and later at Port Arthur—but, in the decades preceding World War I, only the Germans had seen its true potential and provided large numbers for their infantry.

The value of the trench mortar lay in the fact that it provided the infantry with its own portable artillery. It was light in weight, compact, of simple design and easy to manufacture in quantity. Its high-angle fire made it an ideal weapon with which to bombard trenches.

The German trench mortars came in a variety of calibres, ranging from 3-inch to 9·8-inch. The larger types were complex, crew-served weapons. The Allies, outpaced to begin with, launched their trench-mortar programme with a copy of the German model, but by late 1915 the excellent British-designed Newton-Stokes trench mortar was in use at the front.

The range of the trench mortar was short, but in situations where the opposing lines were often no more than 100 yards apart, this was no handicap. The early shells 'tumbled' in their high trajectory and were easily spotted by alert soldiers. This led to the introduction of rifled Minenwerfer and the use of elongated or 'streamlined' shells. These new elongated projectiles in turn prompted the adoption of percussion fuses. The earlier 'billiard-ball'

Types of Barrage Fire in World War I

1: ROLLING BARRAGE

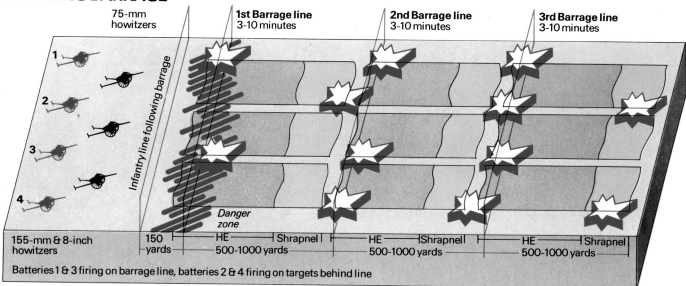

75-mm howitzers

1st Barrage line 3-10 minutes
2nd Barrage line 3-10 minutes
3rd Barrage line 3-10 minutes

Infantry line following barrage

Danger zone

155-mm & 8-inch howitzers

150 yards | HE — Shrapnel 500-1000 yards | HE — Shrapnel 500-1000 yards | HE — Shrapnel 500-1000 yards

Batteries 1 & 3 firing on barrage line, batteries 2 & 4 firing on targets behind line

The rolling barrage was first used in 1915 in an attempt to break the trench warfare stalemate. The barrage was indiscriminate, each battery firing down a 'lane' (roughly 200 yards of front per battery) to a pre-determined barrage line. This barrage line–the 'danger zone'–was always about 150 yards ahead of the infantry advance. Once this line had been pounded for 3–10 minutes (the time it took the infantry to advance 100 yards), the fire was lifted to the next barrage line and then on to the next. The 'jumps' the barrage made were usually 500–1,000 yards deep. Thus the infantry was expected to advance unmolested behind a curtain of high explosive and shrapnel. Heavier guns and howitzers would fire to barrage lines or concentrate on points deeper in enemy-held territory.

In any rolling barrage about one-third of the field guns would fire shrapnel ahead of the HE (shell) barrage line. The divisional artillery would add heavy shrapnel shells but for the most part in their engagements they fired HE.

Rolling barrages were found to be generally ineffective–the enemy simply waited in his bomb-proofs until the barrage line had passed. Besides, they presented tremendous logistical problems for the gunners. It was calculated, for example, that for each 2,500 yards of infantry advance at least one day of artillery preparation was needed; thus the theoretical rate of advance was rarely sustained. By 1918 the advocates of surprise attack had won the day, and some attacks were then made with no artillery preparation whatsoever.

2: BOX BARRAGE

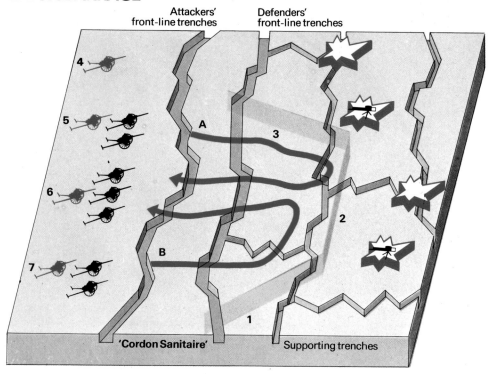

Attackers' front-line trenches

Defenders' front-line trenches

'Cordon Sanitaire'

Supporting trenches

Sequence of fire

1: 75-mm shrapnel barrage
2,3: 75-mm shell barrage, to form 'Cordon Sanitaire'
4,5,6,7: 155-mm shell barrage to neutralize communications trenches and machine-gun emplacements

A,B: Routes of raiding parties

The box barrage was developed late in World War I for use in conjunction with trench raids and infiltration tactics. First, a random preparation was fired. Then, as shown here, the artillery constructed a box or 'cordon sanitaire' with HE and shrapnel around the sector of the enemy's trenches to be raided. The heavier guns and howitzers fired beyond the box at vital points in the enemy's trench network and at machine-gun nests–areas from which the raiding party might be attacked.

3: PROTECTIVE BARRAGE

200 yard
barrage front
per battery

Defenders'
front-line trenches

Attackers'
front-line trenches

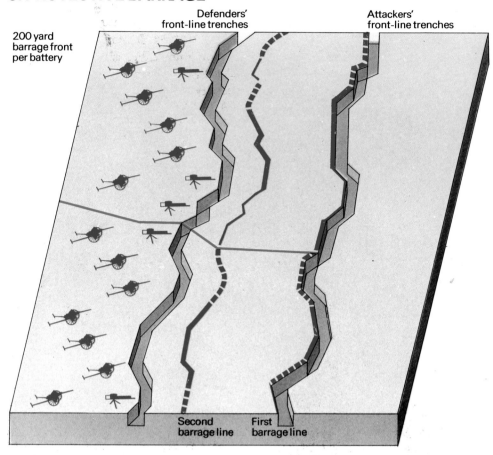

Second
barrage line

First
barrage line

The protective barrage was a technique used throughout 1917, but which almost invariably failed. The idea was to break up attacking lines and destroy the attacker's morale by bringing a sudden, overwhelming concentration of fire to bear on his jump-off point just as his attack began. Lines of approach and attack were plotted and each battery was allotted 200–250 yards of the enemy's front to saturate with a brief but rapid concentration of fire. Later, the barrage line was moved to a point only 150 yards from the trench line to be defended. When it was found that even this was inadequate, because the enemy's forward elements were slipping through with minimal casualties, concentrations just forward of critical points were tried, but, again, there was no diminution of the enemy's ability to drive his attack home. By 1917 this technique was being abandoned in favour of the counter-preparation technique.

4: COUNTER-PREPARATION BARRAGE

Sub-sector
boundary

Defender's
front-line trenches

Potential attackers'
front-line trenches

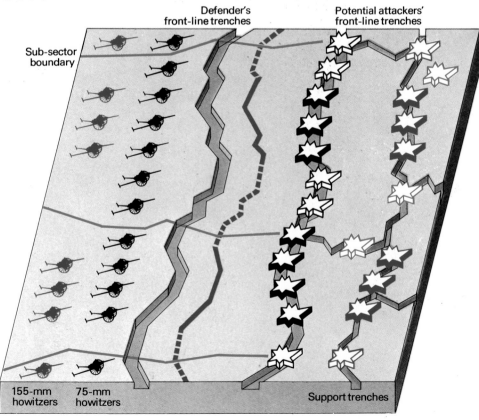

155-mm
howitzers

75-mm
howitzers

Support trenches

The counter-preparation barrage, like the protective barrage, was intended to break up a hostile attacking formation and destroy the morale of the attacker. Some aspects of the protective barrage were retained, but the counter-preparation barrage differed basically in that it was begun the moment an attack was *anticipated or thought probable*. At that moment a saturation fire would be poured onto all possible assembly points, lines of approach and other critical areas of the enemy's line. The fire of each battery, including those of divisional and corps artillery, was predetermined from observation of the enemy's lines.

shells had been fitted with time fuses or a very hazardous 'all-ways' percussion fuse.

Late in the war, when the Germans had perfected infiltration tactics, stormtroopers used Minenwerfer to batter strongpoints. Eight thousand Minenwerfer were used in the German spring offensives of 1918, and much of the latter's early success must be attributed to the skilled use of Minenwerfer by attacking parties.

Not all the tactical surprises of the war sprang from the German camp, however. The Allies managed, for example, to produce a deadly trench mortar-type weapon that the Germans never could quite understand or copy. This was the Livens toxic gas projector. For all the secrecy surround-

ing it, the Livens projector was really a very simple apparatus. Steel tubes with metal base-plates were sunk into the ground in multiple units of 25. A propellant charge was placed at the bottom of each tube, and a drum of poison gas 25-inches long and 8-inches in diameter inserted in each. Then the charges were fired all at once by means of an electric generator. A barrage of drums fired from a bank of such tubes could easily overwhelm a German position. The Livens projector was a great improvement over other modes of gas delivery. The silence of the projector ensured surprise, and the great capacity of the drum gave it a fearsome power, dramatically amplified when a bank was fired simultaneously.

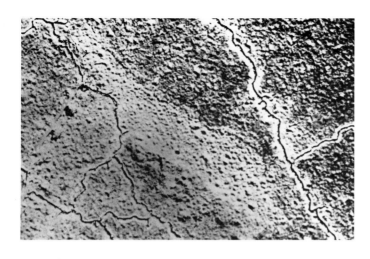

There were basically two schools of thought on how to break the trench-warfare stalemate. One school maintained that the enemy could be worn down and physically defeated in a war of attrition. On the battlefield this policy was translated into long, steady artillery bombardments which 'walked' to and fro over the trenches of the enemy, sometimes lasting for days and weeks on end. The intention was, once the enemy's fortified zone had been sufficiently prepared, for the infantry to advance into the wasteland created by the artillery, effect a breakthrough into open country beyond and restore a war of movement. The chief advocates of the war of attrition were to be found among the Allied High Command.

LEFT *A British 8-inch heavy howitzer in action near Messines. The gun has just been fired and is in partial recoil, running back onto chocks placed behind the wheels.*
TOP *An aerial photograph of shell-pocked terrain on the Western Front. In some areas the ground was so savaged that it has only recently become cultivable.*
ABOVE *One of the monsters that failed to win the war – an Italian gun abandoned to the Germans during the retreat to the Tagliamento in November 1917.*
BELOW *In the Tyrol, an Austrian 75-mm cannon is photographed on its pedestal mount.*

German 210-mm Pariskanone

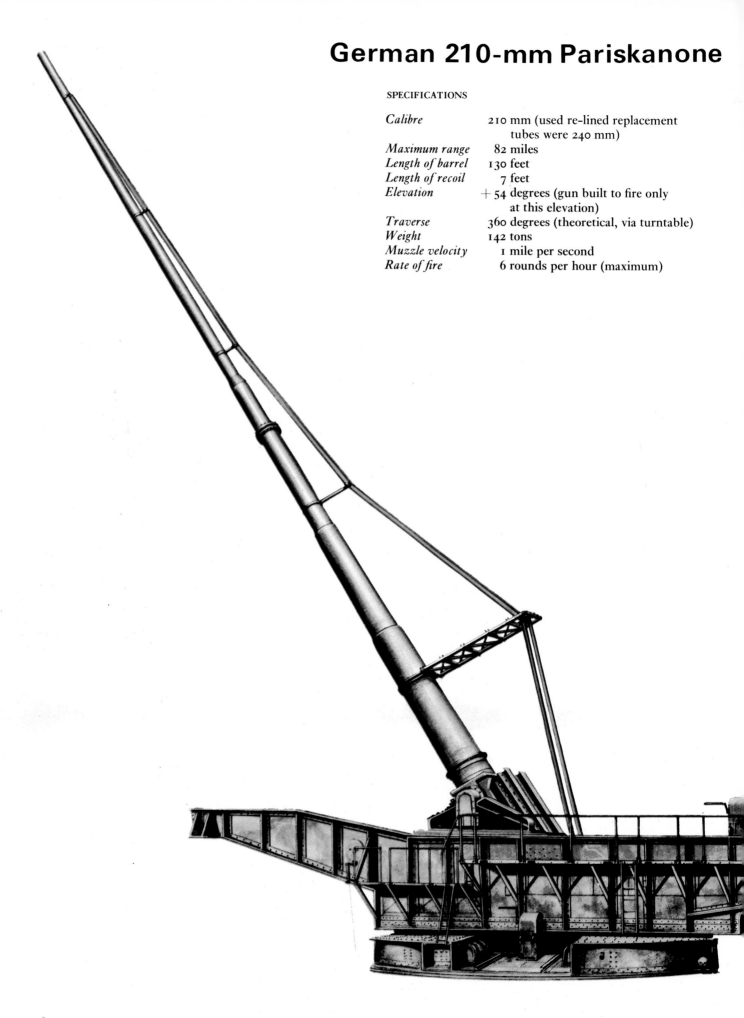

SPECIFICATIONS

Calibre	210 mm (used re-lined replacement tubes were 240 mm)
Maximum range	82 miles
Length of barrel	130 feet
Length of recoil	7 feet
Elevation	+ 54 degrees (gun built to fire only at this elevation)
Traverse	360 degrees (theoretical, via turntable)
Weight	142 tons
Muzzle velocity	1 mile per second
Rate of fire	6 rounds per hour (maximum)

The 'Paris Gun', erroneously called 'Big Bertha' by Allied soldiers, may be the best-known and most mysterious gun of all time. There are few who do not know the story of the bombardment of Paris at a distance of 79 miles from a point 10 miles behind the German lines in the St Gobain Wood near Laon. On the other hand, there are few who know anything about the gun which achieved such an incredible feat.

The Paris Gun was designed by a team of Krupp engineers led by Professor Rausenberger. It (there were three mountings and several barrels) was first used to bombard Paris on 23 March 1918, opening fire at 7.20 am. The bombardment continued intermittently until 7 August 1918. Altogether 203 shells were fired and the majority hit the city. Allied efforts at detecting the guns succeeded in determining their general location despite elaborate efforts to conceal them. Aerial bombardment and long-range shelling of the St Gobain Wood by French railway guns were of no avail, however. Eventually the mountings (but no barrels – they were never found) fell into Allied hands and the shelling of Paris was halted.

The shelling had no noticeable effect on either the French war effort or the people of Paris. To be sure, there was profound shock and horror at the casualties – especially those caused when a shell collapsed the vault of the Church of St Gervais, near the Hôtel de Ville, on Good Friday, 29 March 1918 – but otherwise life went on more or less as usual.

As for the true purpose of the Paris Gun, we shall probably never know. Some speculated that the Germans used it as a terror weapon, hoping to break the morale of the French people. Others felt that its function was to cause people to flee Paris and in doing so disrupt the roads and railways.

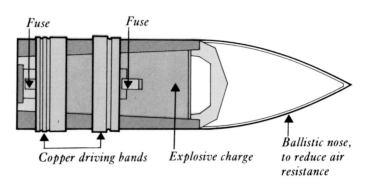

Fuse   *Fuse*

Copper driving bands   *Explosive charge*   *Ballistic nose, to reduce air resistance*

Shell of the Paris Gun

This was a 210-mm HE shell with copper driving bands. The life of each inner gun tube was thought to be 60 rounds, so 60 numbered shells, each a little larger in calibre than the one preceding it (No. 60 was 222 mm), were provided for each barrel and fired in sequence. The weight of the propellant also varied with each shot.

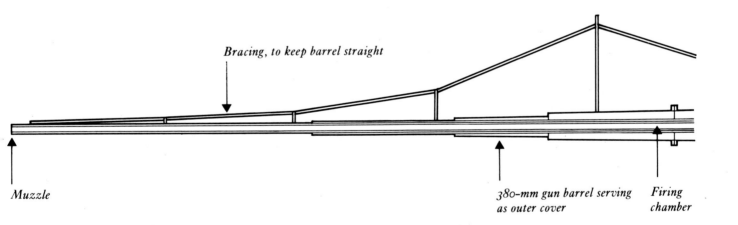

Bracing, to keep barrel straight

Muzzle

380-mm gun barrel serving as outer cover   *Firing chamber*

Barrel of the Paris Gun

Note that the barrel is braced by a suspension system. This was necessary because of the great length and weight of the barrel, which vibrated for two minutes after each firing. (Many long-barrelled, large-calibre guns have a barely perceptible 'droop' in the barrel: this straightens out momentarily on firing.)

The other school favoured sudden, overwhelming artillery barrages of comparatively short duration (hours rather than days) followed by infantry attacks against the defenders while they were still stunned. These tactics were first used by the Germans on the Eastern Front in 1915 and came to characterize most German offensives.

Of the two systems, that developed by the Germans was the more successful. Surprise, an important element in the German system, had always been a decisive factor in warfare. But whereas the Allies assumed that trench warfare had removed surprise from the soldier's 'bag of tricks', the Germans felt that surprise and her handmaiden, confusion, could be achieved by clever artillery tactics. In addition, the simplicity and economy of the German tactics were recommendations in themselves.

The 'hurricane' bombardment, as it became known, was first applied at Dunajec, Galicia on 14 May 1915. There the Germans effected a breakthrough along 26 miles of the Russian lines. After Dunajec the German and Austrian armies used similar tactics time and again to break stable fronts in Serbia, Russia and Italy.

The first Allied attempts at breaking through were conceived as 'limited objective attacks' – though in reality they were limited not only in terms of objective but also in matériel, for the Allies were still inferior in heavy guns; during 1915–16, too, there was a severe shortage of shells. As a result, many of the artillery bombardments were suppressed by German counter-battery fire. Still, there were gains: but they were measured in hundreds of yards and hundreds of thousands of casualties.

By 1917 the Allies had secured industrial supremacy. The guns along their fronts were massed in two or more lines, and expenditure of ammunition reached colossal proportions. Yet numbers alone were not enough. The Germans countered by dispersing their infantry and creating in-depth defences. When Allied soldiers advanced they were additionally impeded by having to cross large shell-torn zones created by their own artillery.

In the meantime, on the Eastern Front, the Russians had adopted the German idea of the surprise bombardment and used it with devastating effect in the six-hour artillery preparation for Brusilov's offensive (4 June 1916). This bombardment completely broke the morale of the Austro-Hungarian 7th Army. The subsequent breakthrough caused the transfer of 45 German and Austrian divisions from the Verdun sector and materially affected the course of the war.

The first use of the surprise bombardment on the Western Front was at Verdun on 21 February 1916. Here, although the bombardment was a success – the German gunners completely shattered the French defences – the main attack was not. The German infantry went forward in driblets, tentatively probing the French lines. The French, given time to recover, held. Thereafter, Verdun became a classic battle of attrition.

ABOVE *General Ludendorff, who master-minded the German spring offensives of 1918.* RIGHT *In September 1916 the tank made its début. Though mechanically unreliable, these lumbering terror weapons helped to restore mobility to the battlefield.* OPPOSITE, BELOW *American infantrymen at the Meuse-Argonne offensive of 1918.*

A sophisticated variant of the surprise bombardment was introduced in September 1917 in the artillery preparation for General Oscar von Hutier's Riga offensive. At Riga, von Hutier coupled his new infiltration tactics for the infantry with clever artillery tactics devised by his artillery commander, Colonel Bruchmüller. Bruchmüller used every gun and Minenwerfer available in a brief but intensive bombardment. Gas shells were fired on an unprecedented scale. Some guns fired on strongpoints, while others fired a rambling barrage which shifted to and fro over the Russian lines. When it was time for von Hutier's stormtroopers to go in, almost all the guns switched to a rolling barrage to cover their advance. The Russians were routed and Riga was taken at comparatively slight cost. Later, when Russia withdrew from the war, the Germans quickly shifted their eastern armies to the Western Front, hoping to use the additional manpower to win the war before the arrival of the American Expeditionary Force.

The spring offensives of 1918, directed by General Ludendorff, used the Hutier-Bruchmüller tactics throughout. These offensives came within an ace of succeeding, but the appearance and rapid impact of the Americans, together with the Allies' artillery superiority, spoiled them in mid-course. By 1918 the Allies had perfected the technique of the counter-preparation bombardment to the extent that German attacks were often broken up before they began. The weight of metal available to the Allies and the rapidity and accuracy with which their guns were fired proved decisive factors in the last year of the war.

Mountain Artillery

In 1914 all the Continental Powers had batteries of mountain guns. These were usually light guns or howitzers which were easily dismantled into six to eight pack-loads for transport by mules over rough terrain. A good crew could have its guns assembled and ready to fire within two minutes of halting its animals.

These mountain batteries not only served in mountainous areas like Galicia or the Italian Front, they were also useful as accompanying artillery for infantry on the offensive. At Verdun in 1916 German field artillery fired at maximum range to prepare the way for the infantry assault. In such situations, the infantry usually went forward without direct support until the field artillery batteries could move forward to new positions. At Verdun, however, batteries of the German Alpine Corps advanced with the infantry and provided close fire support. The idea of accompanying artillery then caught on, and during 1917 the Germans used numbers of *Nahkampfbatterien* (close-combat batteries) with a great variety of equipment, mostly captured field guns.

Because they were usually with the forward elements, these infantry gun batteries inevitably ran foul of the Allied tank effort. The Germans countered by mounting the M-1906 77-mm field gun on low wheels and providing it with AP shells equipped with delay fuses that allowed the shell to burst within the tank.

Later, when von Hutier's infiltration tactics had gained wide acceptance, German shock troops attacked with a full arsenal of artillery firepower including the various Minenwerfer types, and mountain and accompanying guns. Ludendorff, however, seems to have disliked the idea of accompanying batteries and discouraged their use in the great 1918 spring offensives.

LEFT *German mountain guns in use as infantry accompanying weapons.*
BELOW *A gun crew demonstrates how the accompanying guns were moved about in support of an infantry advance.*

Anti-Aircraft Guns

Perhaps the first purpose-built anti-aircraft gun was a single 1-inch 'balloon gun' used by the Germans in the Siege of Paris in 1870. It is not recorded that this contraption ever brought down one of Léon Gambetta's balloons, but there was a lot of speculation in artillery literature before World War I concerning the merits of firing on balloons and Zeppelins with shrapnel. Shooting at balloons was not as easy as the textbooks made it out to be, and aircraft would prove to be an even tougher proposition.

Nevertheless, anti-aircraft guns became common during World War I. Usually, a field gun was coupled with a specially designed mount allowing a high angle of fire or a pedestal or pit mount allowing both high-angle fire and all-round traverse. Various mechanical devices were introduced to allow the gunners to calculate the target's speed, height and direction and correlate this with the fire of the gun. None of these mechanical 'predictors' was very successful, and commanders resorted to area defences and anti-aircraft barrages. An area defence relied on siting

ABOVE *In Salonika, a French 75-mm field gun M-1897 is seen on a special anti-aircraft mount.*
BELOW *On the Italian Front, a British 13-pounder AA gun is mounted on a Peerless truck.*
OPPOSITE *American soldiers examine a captured German AA gun in Oudenarde, November 1918.*

batteries of anti-aircraft guns behind the front in such a manner that when aircraft were detected by sound-ranging equipment, the gun crews were alerted and could then concentrate their fire on the aircraft. Groups of machine guns were sited 1–2,000 yards behind the front line to prevent low-level strafing and observation. Two thousand yards behind the machine guns was a line of regular anti-aircraft batteries sited 4–7,000 yards apart. These guns were to protect the reserve areas. Finally, the rear areas were surrounded by further batteries of anti-aircraft guns.

A different method was used to protect cities or vital points far behind the lines. In this sytem batteries were sited along the lines of approach commonly used by aircraft. The anti-aircraft batteries protecting Paris, for example, were sited along the rivers and rail lines leading to the city. Since aircraft navigational devices were still quite crude, pilots used natural or man-made features of the terrain as their principal means of guidance, and this brought them in range of the guns. However, the system could only be called partly successful: on average one aircraft was brought down for every 3,000 shells fired!

Railway Guns

Railway artillery had been introduced during the American Civil War and was used extensively in World War I. Such guns could be used only in certain specific situations. They were ideal for coastal defence or on static fronts where the existing rail system was adequate enough to allow them to be used where they were most needed.

The French had the most advanced railway-gun programme before the war, and during the war they converted many ex-naval and coastal guns to railway mounts. The country's excellent rail system allowed them to use these guns for support fire, raking the enemy's lines of communications, and in long-range counter-battery work. The presence of a supplementary, mobile artillery arm was especially valued among the French, who were generally weak in heavy guns.

Among the few guns which the United States sent to Europe were three 14-inch battleship guns on special armoured railway mounts. These guns were manned by Navy personnel and fired 782 projectiles during the last days of the war. They are credited with destroying a German supply depot at Laon and with cutting the Metz-Sedan railway at several points.

Thus, railway guns made an important contribution to the Allied war effort. Within the next few decades, however, the potential of aerial bombardment would relegate the monster railway and coastal-defence guns to obscurity.

BELOW *Because of its railway mounting this battery of French heavy guns gained enormously in mobility and flexibility.*
OPPOSITE, TOP *The USA sent three naval railway batteries to France, each comprising one gun plus ammunition and auxiliary carriages; their targets were rail and supply centres behind the German lines. Shown here is a 14-inch gun Mark 2.*

ABOVE *A camouflaged 305-mm railway gun on the Western Front; from a painting by Rudolf Stanley-Brown.*

Chapter Four
The Inter-War Years

Dr Vannevar Bush, the brilliant scientist who directed the US Office of Scientific Research and Development during World War II, once wrote that 'there is something about the word ordnance that produces stodginess in its adherents . . . this is not a matter of this country alone; it seems to be a general affliction'. Although it is partly understandable in a peacetime situation, at no time was the 'stodginess', or conservatism, of the artillerist more evident than during the inter-war years.

A dangerous complacency appeared in the wake of World War I. To most observers, especially the French, the defence had triumphed decisively. Against this view the lessons inherent in the successes of the early tanks, the possibilities to be derived from coupling Bruchmüller's use of artillery with von Hutier's infiltration tactics, indeed any comprehension of a war of movement such as had just taken place in the Middle East and during the final Allied offensive, seemed beyond the capabilities of the general staffs of most nations. Ordnance development ground to a halt.

In Germany, however, there was no drag on development. Even during the Weimar period, when the country's armed strength was limited by the Treaty of Versailles, there were those who planned for the day when Germany should once again assume her place as a major power. Much ordnance development during these years was of the 'black' variety, which is to say it was private and unsolicited by the army authorities.

OPPOSITE *US coast artillery drill: soldiers receive and chalk up instructions relayed to them from the plotting room.*
ABOVE *Manoeuvres with '75s' at Fort Meyer, Virginia, in 1929.*
BELOW *A ½-ton shell, delivered by trolley, is rammed into the breech during an artillery drill session.*

These clandestine programmes surfaced and bore fruit after Hitler came to power in 1933. In due course the great munitions makers like Krupp and Rheinmetall functioned as easily under Hitler as they had under the Hohenzollerns; they even enjoyed a favoured position in German industry as the firms that were to bear the great brunt of German re-armament.

At that time the Germans had to rebuild their artillery from almost nothing. The Treaty of Versailles had stripped away most of Germany's World War I stock of guns on the pretext of denying her a war-making capability. What this in effect did was to remove the 'tail' of previous development – a large inventory of outdated guns which would otherwise have inevitably postponed new development.

As an example of how rapidly the German arms makers developed radically new guns we need only cite the story of the 88-mm anti-aircraft/anti-tank (AA/AT) gun Flak 18. Work on this versatile gun was officially begun in 1933 – though there is evidence of co-operative 'black' development during the 1920s between the firms of Krupp in Germany and Bofors in Sweden[1]. By 1934 the first models

[1] Bofors' projects during this period also included building LK II tanks under licence for the Germans.

of the '88' were delivered to the Wehrmacht, and when the gun was fully unveiled in the Spanish Civil War (1936–39), its capabilities astounded the military world. It was in this way that Germany entered World War II with a completely new range of artillery weapons, thoroughly modern and quite superior to that of any prospective rival.

Another nation steadily renewing her artillery was the Soviet Union. The Soviets opted for simple design, mobility and performance in their new family of guns; this policy helped them to rebuild at speed, and when, in June 1941, the storm of Operation Barbarossa broke on their western border, they were well on their way towards completing the process. Two main factors drove the Russians along in their re-equipment programme. One was the relative absence of modern medium and heavy artillery in the Czarist stockpile inherited by the revolutionary regime. The second was the growing likelihood of war with Hitler's Germany.

Compared with the way the totalitarian states mobilized their industrial potential for war, the Western democracies, the victors of World War I, did little to modernize or replace their existing artillery stockpiles. France, for example, entered World War II with virtually the same artillery establishment as she possessed in 1918. Great Britain was well supplied with field artillery but possessed no heavy guns comparable to those of the Germans. Had the United States been attacked in 1939, her situation would have been similar to that of Great Britain.

Despite their innate conservatism artillerists, like all professionals, need to get together every now and then (usually after a war) and review their general situation. World War I had produced a few lessons which were readily appreciated by almost everyone. These lessons had chiefly to do with how one uses the guns at one's disposal. There were few who actually questioned the utility of some of the guns, but one group that did was the Westervelt Board, a US study group which met in 1919. The Westervelt Board concluded that the light field guns which formed the bulk of any nation's artillery park were not especially useful. It recommended the replacement of the M-1897 75-mm guns of the US Army by a 105-mm gun-howitzer. The latter would combine the low-trajectory capability of the field gun with the ability of the howitzer to fire mid-angle 'searching' shots. By 1939 every Western nation but France had replaced field guns with gun-howitzers.

Anti-tank weapons represented a comparatively new field. As late as 1922, US artillery manuals described anti-tank guns as 'guns detached from batteries and pushed forward for individual use against tanks'. However, anti-tank gun development was not regarded as a top-priority matter and little real progress was made. Nevertheless, one project – the German Gerlich gun – deserves a closer look.

(over 4,000 fps) imparted to the tungsten-carbide projectile it fired. This gun was among the first produced which utilized the Gerlich-pattern barrel. Its super-high-velocity projectile was capable of penetrating the armour of any tank in the world.

The story of the Gerlich gun begins in Weimar Germany. A Kiel engineer, Max Gerlich, had been tinkering with the application to field guns of the coned-bore principle, which had been used in hunting rifles for several decades. By 1933 Gerlich had perfected his gun. The extraordinarily high muzzle velocity was produced as the shell was forced down the barrel of the gun. The shell itself had a core of diamond-hard tungsten carbide. Around this core were a series of rings or flanges of a light alloy. The flanges conformed to the breech calibre, and, when the gun was fired, they were squeezed down into grooves behind them and around the core. This squeezing-down of the projectile as it travelled down the barrel concentrated an exceptionally long explosive impulse on the ever-decreasing base area of the shell. The result was a muzzle velocity much greater than that produced with conventional weapons.

The Germans, characteristically, disguised the development of their experimental Gerlich guns by putting about rumours of a high-velocity shell which they styled the 'Hagar Ultra Shell'. Strangely though, from the point of view of national security, Gerlich himself had travelled

OPPOSITE Even after the invasion of Russia in 1941, armies still depended on equipment developed several years earlier: an example is this German 37-mm Pak 35/36 anti-tank gun.
ABOVE German '88s', first tested in the Spanish Civil War, here take on enemy tanks in Russia; from a painting by Preuss.
BELOW The Gerlich gun: its tapering bore squeezed the projectile, and muzzle velocity was much improved.

On 6 April 1942 a British newspaper correspondent covering the North African campaign filed a story on a new, 'particularly revolutionary' German anti-tank gun. The Allies had captured a diminutive, sleek-looking gun with a barrel that tapered from 28-mm at the breech to 21-mm at the muzzle. The revolutionary aspects of this gun were its coned-bore design and the tremendous muzzle velocity

abroad on several earlier occasions to try and sell his invention to other nations. It seems, however, that only the German War Office was interested in his progressive ideas. The first production models of Gerlich's gun were built by Krupp in 1941, when it was designated as the 2·8-cm Schwere (heavy) Panzerbüchse 41.

With the exception of the experimental Gerlich gun development in Germany, most nations seemed content with what they had in the way of anti-tank guns during the 1930s. The day of the gun-armour race had not yet dawned, and light anti-tank guns like the French Hotchkiss 25-mm gun were perfectly adequate against under-armoured early tanks – even though the latter's performance was laughable by World War II standards. The advocates of armour were not standing still, however, and where they had the ear of an attentive government, as in Germany and Russia, they were teaming up with designers to produce radical new tanks – heavier, faster and more powerful than many men imagined possible.

The result of these revolutionary developments in tank design and doctrine, combined with the staunch conservatism of the artillerists, produced some ghastly consequences less than a decade later. Many British anti-tank gunners in Libya, for example, were subjected to the unnerving and often fatal spectacle of German Mark III tanks stopping 600 yards from their emplacements (200 yards

beyond the effective range of their 2-pounder AT guns) and pounding them with armour-piercing machine-gun fire which easily penetrated their gun shields.

Even the Germans, who led the world in anti-tank gun development during the 1930s, were not unsurpassable. They too were thrown into confusion when they encountered the first Russian T-34 tanks in 1941. These superb vehicles were the product of inter-war Russian tank design, and the Germans in effect never entirely recovered from the set-backs they experienced during the Russian winter of 1941.

The Spanish Civil War (1936–39) proved to be a significant rehearsal ground for World War II. The Soviet Union, supporting the Republic, and the Fascist powers of Germany and Italy, supporting Franco's Nationalists, all sent men and equipment to Spain. Hitler's Kondor Legion arrived with the latest products of Germany's rearmament programme, including light tanks, Stuka dive-bombers and the '88'. German weapons and tactical doctrine received a

OPPOSITE, ABOVE *The Stuka, or dive-bomber, another of Hitler's weapons pre-tested in Spain for the Blitzkrieg to come.*
OPPOSITE, BELOW *Knocked-out Polish anti-tank guns, overwhelmed by the ferocity of the German onslaught levelled at them by land and from the air in September 1939.*
BELOW *British troops man a Hotchkiss 25-mm anti-tank gun; the latter soon became obsolete as tank armour was increased.*

thorough test, and a few valuable lessons were learned. It was found, for example, that the map-firing stressed by artillery instructors was often best forgotten in real conditions; in combat it was the forward observer who became the key figure in directing a battery's fire. The Kondor Legion was also able to try out its new radio equipment, which added flexibility and increased the effectiveness of its guns. Previously, the time taken to lay the miles of telephone wire connecting the various field and gun commanders and the FOOs (forward observations officers) had been time wasted. Yet another lesson pointed to the ineffectiveness of counter-battery fire without aerial observation. Again, to be really successful, the Kondor Legion's commanders saw that in any future war there would have to be wireless communication between the guns and aircraft.

In the course of the Spanish Civil War anti-tank guns were used extensively for the first time. Here the light inter-war models proved adequate against the assortment of light tanks and armoured cars fielded by the belligerents. But no unified anti-tank doctrine was formulated, and stopping tanks was still a matter of luck more than anything else. Thus, when World War II began, none of the Great Powers had developed a clear-cut plan for dealing with masses of tanks; this was a near-disastrous flaw from which both sides were to suffer in the armoured conflicts to come.

The Artillery War 1939–1945

A Chronology

THE SYMBOL ☐ DENOTES ACTIVITY OVER A PERIOD OF TIME

1939

SEPTEMBER
1 Germany invades Poland in first Blitzkrieg campaign.
3 Britain and France declare war on Germany.
17 Soviet invasion of Poland.

OCTOBER
12 First divisions of British Expeditionary Force join Allied line at Lille.

NOVEMBER
4 Repeal of US Neutrality Law; materials of war sold to Britain on cash-and-carry basis.
30 Soviet invasion of Finland.

1940

FEBRUARY
1-13 Russian assault on Mannerheim Line launched by tremendous preparatory bombardment; reduces Finnish morale and makes breakthrough possible.

APRIL
9 Germany occupies Denmark; landings at six cities in Norway.

MAY
10 Germany invades France and Low Countries in second major Blitzkrieg operation.
16-21 German drive to the Channel.
26 Start of Dunkirk evacuation (Operation Dynamo); completed on 4 June.

JUNE
4 Start of Allied evacuation of Norway; completed on 10th.
10 Italy joins war on Germany's side.
14 Germans enter Paris; armistice signed on 22nd.

JULY
10 Battle of Britain begins.
16 Hitler issues directive for plan to invade Britain (Operation Sea Lion).

SEPTEMBER
13 Marshal Graziani invades Egypt.
17 Operation Sea Lion indefinitely postponed after failure of Luftwaffe to defeat RAF.
27 Axis pact signed in Berlin by Germany, Italy and Japan.

OCTOBER
28 Italy invades Greece.

DECEMBER
9 General O'Connor leads Western Desert Force against Italians in North Africa.

1941

FEBRUARY
6-7 Fall of Benghazi, 20,000 Italians surrender.
12 General Rommel arrives in Tripoli.

MARCH
11 Passing of Lend Lease Act by USA.
24 Rommel begins first offensive at El Agheila; encircles Tobruk on 13 April.

JUNE
22 Germany invades USSR (Operation Barbarossa).

JULY
9 Minsk falls to German armoured pincer; Smolensk taken on 15th– Germans capture 100,000 Russians.
24 Japan secures 'protection rights' from France over Indo-China.

SEPTEMBER
8 Leningrad cut off by German tanks.
19 Fall of Kiev.
26 Moscow offensive resumed; progress slowed by onset of winter.

OCTOBER
21 General Zhukov takes command of Moscow's outer defences.

NOVEMBER
18 General Auchinleck's offensive begins in North Africa.
☐ Defence of Moscow and beginning of Russian counter-offensive.

DECEMBER
7 Japanese attack Pearl Harbor, Malaya and Siam (Thailand).
8 USA declares war on Axis powers.
10 Japanese invade Philippines.
11 Germany and Italy declare war on USA.

1942

JANUARY
9 Russian counter-blows reach Smolensk province.
21 Rommel's second offensive forces British withdrawal beyond Benghazi.

FEBRUARY
15 Singapore surrenders to Japanese after intensive aerial and artillery bombardment.

MARCH
15-21 Japanese bombardment of Forts Frank and Drum (the 'concrete battleship') in Manila Bay.
24 Intensive air and artillery bombardment of US positions on Bataan Peninsula demoralizes defenders.

APRIL
8 Fall of Bataan.
10 Siege of Corregidor begins; falls on 6 May.

MAY
8 Germans launch spring offensive on Eastern Front.

JUNE
4-6 Battle of Midway.
7 Operation Sturgeon–German conquest of Crimea; Krupp 80-cm 'Gustav' bombards Sebastopol in largest German artillery concentration of war.
14-30 British retreat into Egypt.
28 Germans launch summer offensive in Russia.

AUGUST
7 US landings on Guadalcanal; island cleared by February 1943.
13 General Montgomery takes over command of Eighth Army, now in El Alamein position.
24 Fighting begins in and around Stalingrad.

OCTOBER
23-24 Artillery preparation for British advance at El Alamein.

NOVEMBER
4 British breakthrough at El Alamein.
8 Operation Torch–Anglo-American landings in North Africa.
19-23 Soviet counter-offensive against German centre; German Sixth Army cut off.

1943

JANUARY
5 First use of VT (proximity) fuses in shells fired from US cruiser *Helena* against Japanese aircraft.

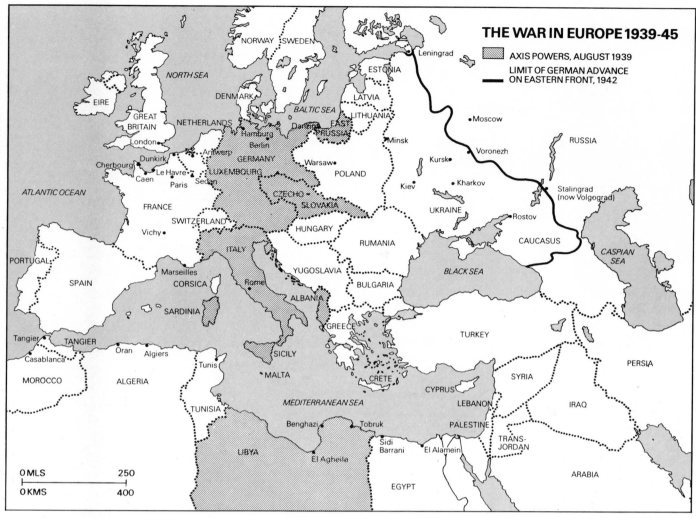

THE WAR IN EUROPE 1939-45

▨ AXIS POWERS, AUGUST 1939

━━ LIMIT OF GERMAN ADVANCE
ON EASTERN FRONT, 1942

FEBRUARY

2   German Sixth Army capitulates in Stalingrad.

2-20   Russian drive across the Donets.

FEBRUARY–MARCH

☐   General von Manstein organizes German counter-offensive, recaptures Kharkov on 14 March.

MAY

3-13   Battle of Tunisia ends Axis presence in North Africa.

JUNE

☐   Anglo-American bomber offensive launched against Germany.

JULY

4-16   Battle of Kursk: Russian AT guns destroy 40% of German armoured attack force. German Panzerarmee crippled beyond repair.

10   Allied landings on Sicily.

SEPTEMBER

3   Allied landings in mainland Italy.

8   Italian armistice, signed on 3rd, becomes effective; Germans begin to disarm and imprison Italian troops.

DECEMBER

☐   Soviet winter offensive; Russians fortified by new T-34 tanks mounting 85-mm gun.

☐   German V-weapon (rocket) bombardment of Britain.

1944

JANUARY

5-15   Drive to Rapido River in Italy. Appearance of new American heavy guns gives Allies superiority in heavy artillery for first time in war.

22   Anzio operations: 'Anzio Annie' and 'Anzio Express', German 28-cm railway guns in action; 73% of Allied casualties due to German artillery and mortar fire.

MAY–JUNE

☐   Allied breakthrough in Italy and advance on Rome.

JUNE

6   Allied invasion of Normandy (Operation Overlord).

22   Massive Russian assault on German Army Group Centre with 400 guns per mile of front.

JULY

1-24   Expansion of Normandy beachhead.

10   Russians begin drive into Poland.

21   US landings on Guam.

AUGUST

1   General Patton's Third Army breaks out of Cherbourg peninsular.

25   Liberation of Paris.

OCTOBER

21   Allies breach Siegfried Line.

DECEMBER

8   Start of US pre-invasion bombardment of Iwo Jima.

16   Hitler launches Ardennes counter-offensive. First land use of VT fuse against German troops in Battle of Bulge.

1945

FEBRUARY

13-14   Bombing of Dresden.

16   First US carrier raids on Japan.

MARCH

7   US 9th Armoured Division seizes Remagen Bridge and makes first Allied crossing of Rhine.

APRIL

1   US landings on Okinawa; cleared 21 June.

16   Russian guns fire on Berlin.

MAY

8   Unconditional German surrender.

AUGUST

6/9   Atomic bombing of Japan.

8   USSR declares war on Japan.

SEPTEMBER

2   Japanese instrument of surrender signed aboard US battleship *Missouri* in Tokyo Bay.

Chapter Five

World War II

World War I had been a fairly straightforward conflict in which the duties of the artillerist had remained for the most part what they had always been. A new form of artillery had been introduced in an attempt to counter aircraft, and crude beginnings had been made towards solving the problem of the tank.

World War II was another matter. All the belligerents were quickly drawn into a deadly race against technological defeat, and both guns and gunners now had to be adaptable to a variety of changing conditions and environments. Understandably, too, the circumstances of individual campaigns rendered some weapons obsolete and thrust others into prominence.

Anti-aircraft and anti-tank guns were developed to near optimum efficiency during the war. Rocket artillery was revived and used extensively for area fire. Mobility was improved through the use of self-propelled mounts and motor traction. And the amount of firepower available to local commanders increased dramatically in two ways; firstly, the use of shaped-charge projectiles, rocket weapons and recoilless guns enabled the infantryman to carry his own artillery with him; and, secondly, the support of radio and aerial observation enabled the artillery to assist other arms quickly, accurately and decisively. In this way artillery became an important strike element, indeed a force without which no operation would be contemplated.

The artillery of the Great Powers in World War II may be summarized as follows:

France. The Puteaux '75' was still the standard field gun in 1940. Various modernizations, including 'high-speed' wheels and 'streamline' shells, had improved its cross-country mobility and range. The medium and heavy guns were for the most part late-World War I or immediately post-war models. In keeping with French tactical doctrine, which stressed positional warfare, there was a decided lack of mobility among the larger calibres. The French firms of St Chamond and Schneider had pioneered the development of large-calibre self-propelled (SP) guns during World War I, and many of their models were in action during the Battle of France. These SP guns were not armoured and they were slow by World War II standards. Most of them were destroyed by dive-bombers or lost to the rapid movements of the Panzers.

The French artillery was totally unprepared for the task facing it in May 1940. The Germans were struck by the inability of French gunners to cope with the conditions of

modern warfare. Field Marshal Erich von Manstein later recorded his 'pleasant surprise' at discovering the weaknesses of French artillery:

Their shooting was not adaptable enough, and their speed in putting down strong concentrations of fire fell far short of the standard required in a war of movement. What was more, they had not developed forward observation technique to anything like the same extent as we had. . . .

(from *Lost Victories*, by Erich von Manstein)

If the effort of the French field artillery was bad, their anti-tank and anti-aircraft measures were worse. The anti-tank guns are covered elsewhere; as for the anti-aircraft defences, the French General A.V. Georges described them as 'non-existent'.

Great Britain. The very advanced 25-pounder gun-howitzer had replaced the World War I vintage 18-pounder field gun and the 4·5-inch howitzer as the standard field artillery weapon by the time the North African campaign began. The 25-pounder was a remarkable weapon with a number of exceptional features. It could be emplaced in one minute, had a lightweight firing platform which allowed rapid all-round traverse (a valuable asset when fighting tanks) and replaceable tube-liners that could be quickly changed in the field.

OPPOSITE *Before the Fall, 1940: a French 194-mm self-propelled gun lumbers across country. Slow and of basically World War I vintage, the French SP guns were destroyed in droves during the May–June fighting by German dive-bombers and by fast-moving Panzer units.*
BELOW Vormarsch! *German troops pour at speed through a gap in the French defences; from a painting by Handel-Mazzoti.*

ABOVE *Gun crew of the US Eleventh Corps Artillery fire an 8-inch howitzer ('Comanche') on pockets of Japanese resistance on Ipo Dam Hill, Luzon, 26 May 1945.*
LEFT AND RIGHT *British 25-pounders operating in the Western Desert, 1942.*

The elderly 6-inch howitzer remained the standard British medium howitzer for a time and was used with great effectiveness in the counter-battery role in North Africa (where the Germans had few comparable weapons). But it was obsolete by World War II standards and was in due course replaced by the excellent 5·5-inch gun.

British heavy guns were mostly World War I leftovers. They were notable for their lack of mobility even by pre-war standards, and (fortunately) most had to be left in France following the Dunkirk evacuation. In later campaigns the British relied chiefly on modern US 'heavies'.

The British anti-tank effort was similarly handicapped by obsolescent material, but the introduction in 1942 of the 6-pounder AT gun and, a short while later, the 17-pounder, helped to redress the balance. The 3·7-inch AA gun, like the US 90-mm AA gun, was eventually used in many roles and became Britain's best anti-tank gun.

USA. The guns and howitzers of World War I, be they of French or British parentage, were gradually replaced by newer designs following the recommendations of the Westervelt Board of 1919. By the time US participation in World War II seemed likely, US designers had produced a 105-mm howitzer – the famous M–2 – which has remained standard equipment to this day. The older '75s' were gradually replaced by this gun. Corps and army artillery were equipped with the 105-mm and a new 155-mm howitzer M–1.

The long-range guns included the 155-mm M–1 A–1 'Long Tom', the 8-inch gun M–1, the 240-mm howitzer M–1 and the 8-inch howitzer M–1. The 'Long Tom' was a direct descendant of the 155-mm GPF gun of World War I, but had been so improved that it was far superior to other mobile 'heavies' produced during the war. It was ready by 1938 and provided accurate fire to a range of 25,000 yards.

The 8-inch gun used the same carriage as the 240-mm howitzer, which was first used in Italy in 1943. These guns and the 8-inch howitzer greatly increased the strength of Allied heavy artillery. The 8-inch howitzer gained a reputation as the most accurate gun used in the war and was often called upon to deliver destructive pin-point fire on bridges and strongpoints in the enemy's rear that even bombers could not destroy.

The 90-mm 'Baby Long Tom' AA gun was the most prominent of the group of anti-aircraft guns used by US forces during the war. This versatile gun was equally effective as an anti-tank, anti-aircraft or field gun – a facility which earned it the affectionate nickname of 'Triple Threat Gun'. In the Pacific theatre it was used to 'snipe' at Japanese pill-boxes and bunkers, while in Europe it played a central role in defeating the V-1 raids on London and Antwerp. Of 5,000 V-1s aimed at Antwerp alone, only 211 penetrated the 90-mm AA defences.

The effectiveness of the 90-mm gun was so complete that it was found unnecessary to provide the larger 120-mm AA gun for overseas deployment. The 120-mm AA gun had been built to counter anticipated German high-altitude bombing raids on the USA. It had an effective ceiling of 56,000 feet. Both the 90-mm and 120-mm AA guns were built to receive radar data and had complex electric directors and fire-control equipment.

The USA fielded a representative group of anti-tank guns ranging from the 37-mm M-3 to the 3-inch M-5. The 57-mm M-1, the gun most commonly used in the field, was a light and useful piece but it could not cope with the heavier German armour encountered towards the end of the war. The 90-mm AA gun was frequently found in an anti-tank role during the last campaigns.

TOP *A US 240-mm howitzer emplaced near San Vittore, Italy.*
ABOVE *The crew of 'Lottie', a US 105-mm howitzer, receives firing data by telephone from an air spotter.*
BELOW *Americans under fire hit the dirt beside a 57-mm AT gun.*

USSR. Stalin characterized artillery as the 'god of war', and events on the Eastern Front fully confirmed his assertion. Nowhere in World War II was artillery used in such massive concentrations and with such destructive effect as in the titanic battles on the steppes of Russia and Eastern Europe.

The Soviets entered World War II with the beginnings, at least, of a fully modern arsenal, a very advanced tactical doctrine for the artillery, and a great deal of practical experience. The experience had been gained in the Russo-Finnish War (1939–40) and in fighting the Japanese in Manchuria, most notably at the great Battle of Khalkin Gol (1939). There, the need for camouflage and manoeuvrability – skills not easily mastered in peacetime excercises – had been rudely taught by the Japanese aviators.

In 1941, Soviet artillery doctrine was conceptually far in advance of that of the other Great Powers. This doctrine had been promulgated in the mid-1930s. Its chief tenets were:

1 *All defence is primarily anti-tank defence, and all artillery is anti-tank artillery.*

All Russian guns, whatever their formal designation – gun, howitzer or AT gun – had formidable AT capabilities. Insistence on an AT capability had led the Soviets to retain large numbers of field guns in their divisional artillery. They had not whole-heartedly embraced the new 'gun-how' (see page 74). In the Soviet system even their howitzers, which had little chance of knocking out a tank, were to lay down barrage fire to separate the accompanying infantrymen from their tanks and to harass the tanks with HE shells. After the early setbacks of Operation Barbarossa, when it was driven almost to the gates of Moscow, the Red Army introduced lighter field guns and adopted the concept of in-depth defence first introduced by a German, von Lossberg, in 1917. The most sophisticated defence of this type was created in the Kursk salient in 1943.

2 *In offensive operations, direct fire from masses of guns should be encouraged, and area-fire weapons used extensively.*

The Soviets regarded artillery as the main strike force of any army or 'front' (army group). As in other armies, once the point of main effort had been determined, the artillery was placed well forward to deal with the enemy's guns. The Russians discouraged fire at ranges beyond 6–8 miles. Their artillery preparations were usually either long, rhythmical bombardments or were of the surprise 'drum-fire' type. Soviet insistence on the strike capability of artillery led to the formation of a unique artillery organization beyond divisional and corps levels. This was the artillery reserve of the High Command, a powerful reserve of medium and heavy guns which was used to form artillery 'fists'. Such 'fists' were allocated to important offensive operations which sometimes involved more than 20,000 pieces.

Russian guns and howitzers were of simple design, rugged construction and crude finish. Soviet gunsights and optical equipment were comparatively primitive but were considered to be more accurate than the guns they served. These were factors which may well have contributed to the emphasis on direct fire in Soviet tactical doctrine. Similarly, the poor state of development of Soviet electronic technology did not allow the development of complex electronic directors and computers or radar range-finders for the anti-aircraft artillery, although such devices were in common use among the Western Allies.

TOP *Abandoned Soviet guns at Petroskaja. In the background is a 122-mm field gun M-1937 with its towing tractor. In the foreground is a wrecked 76-mm field gun M-1939.*
ABOVE *Soviet howitzers during the defence of Moscow. Here, in the cruel winter of 1941, the Germans received a major setback.*
BELOW *A Soviet 122-mm howitzer M-1938. This howitzer was widely used both in World War II and in Korea (1950–53). The recoil mechanism is sited in the cradle below the tube, and the recuperator is carried above it.*

German 88-mm Flak Gun

The famous German '88' was developed from designs worked out under a co-operative arrangement between the firms of Krupp and Bofors in the 1920s, and was first produced under Hitler (who became Führer in 1934). The gun first saw action in the Spanish Civil War, and its World War II career is well known.

The '88' type was comparatively advanced when it was first introduced, but gradually other nations produced guns which were its equivalent if not better. Among these were the US 90-mm AA gun and the British 3·7-inch AA gun.

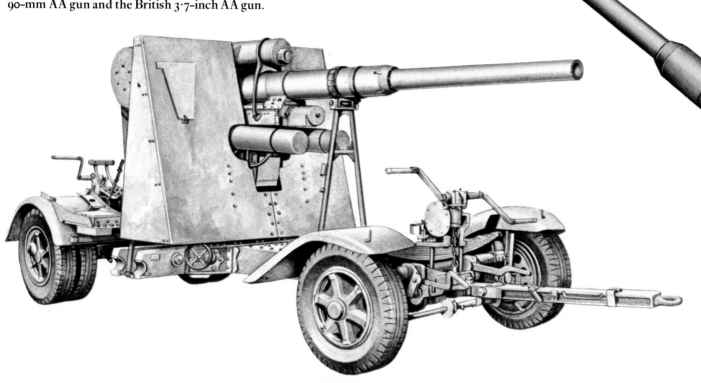

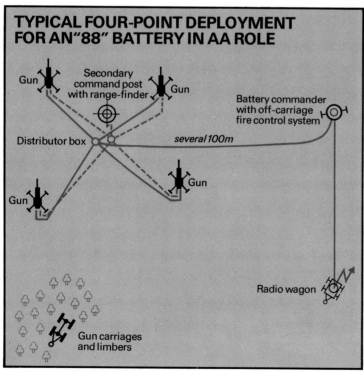

TYPICAL FOUR-POINT DEPLOYMENT FOR AN "88" BATTERY IN AA ROLE

Gun

Secondary command post with range-finder

Gun

Battery commander with off-carriage fire control system

Distributor box

several 100m

Gun

Gun

Radio wagon

Gun carriages and limbers

ABOVE *The '88' as it was used by German forces in North Africa to destroy the tanks of the Allies. The gun also served with distinction on the Eastern Front against the Russian armour.*

Much of the 88-mm gun's fame rests not on its performance as a flak, or anti-aircraft, gun but rather on its use as an anti-tank weapon. Its potency in this role was first noticed in Spain, where, although deployed as an AA weapon, it was often called upon to deal with tanks that had broken into front-line positions. During World War II, in North Africa and Russia, the '88' was more often than not employed primarily in the AT role. This was especially true in Russia during the period of Operation Barbarossa when it was found that the '88' was the only German gun capable of dealing with the new Russian T-34 and KV tanks.

SPECIFICATIONS

Calibre	88 mm
Range	35,700 feet (maximum vertical)
	34,770 feet (effective ceiling)
	16,600 yards (maximum horizontal)
Weight in action	4·9 tons
Weight in draught	7·1 tons
Length of barrel	56 calibres (16 feet 1·8 inches)
Elevation	− 3 to + 85 degrees
Traverse	2 × 360 degrees
Muzzle velocity	2,755 fps
Rate of fire	25 rpm (theoretical)
	12−15 rpm (practical)
Weight of projectile	20·1 pounds or 20·3 pounds (HE)
	21 pounds (AP)
Weight of complete round	31·7 pounds or 32 pounds (HE)
	33 pounds (AP)

LEFT *The '88' seen in the role for which it was originally built – as a Flak or anti-aircraft gun.*

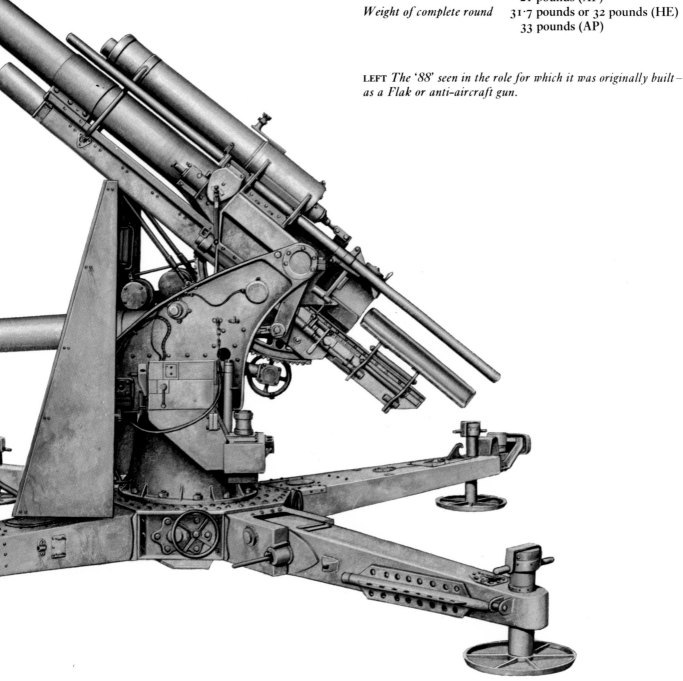

Germany. The superiority of the German Army's organization, training and tactical doctrine carried it to its early victories and sustained it in its darkest hours. Initially, too, the Germans possessed superior weaponry. But as the war progressed, the Allies fielded guns superior to the excellent German pre-war models. By late 1942, German superiority in matériel had been overcome in most areas.

The tendency has been for many commentators to ascribe the early successes of the German Army to its superior weapons. The best example of this phenomenon seems to be the almost mythical aura surrounding the 88-mm AA/AT gun. In reality, however, the reasons for Germany's successes must be sought elsewhere. And, in the context of artillery, a great deal must be attributed to the Germans' advanced tactical thinking.

German tactical doctrine laid great stress on the role of the forward observer. Artillery observers accompanied the infantry in its advance, rode in specially equipped radio tanks with armoured elements, and surveyed the turmoil of the fighting front from Feiseler Storch observation planes. Although most communication was by wire, the radio was used extensively in mobile operations.

Flexibility and co-operation of arms were at the heart of the German system, and unit commanders were taught to be 'artillery minded' – to rely in all instances upon the close-support fire of their artillery. The close-support function was usually carried out by the divisional artillery's three battalions of 105-mm howitzers (model 1eFH 18); a later model, the 1eFH 44, was a considerable improvement and out-ranged all other light howitzers then in service. Each German artillery division also had a medium battalion equipped with 15-cm howitzers and 15-cm guns. The medium battalion engaged in counter-battery work and general fire support.

The German Army had no corps artillery as such, but if a concentration of guns was required for an operation, groups of guns would be created or assembled from those available. There was a complement of heavy guns available, one of the most famous and most feared being the 17-cm K-18, an excellent long-range piece. Until the appearance of the US 8-inch gun in 1942, this gun outranged all the mobile heavy ordnance of the Allies.

OPPOSITE, TOP *An Italian mobile AA gun in action on the North African coast, 1942.*
LEFT *German horse-drawn artillery on the Eastern Front. The use of the horse in this role had seemed archaic to many as early as 1918, and the Germans have been frequently criticized for their astonishing dependence upon horse-drawn artillery and wagons during World War II.*
ABOVE *Standing in sharp contrast to the horse-drawn vehicles – the vastly more dependable Krauss-Maffei prime mover. Next to the tractor is a Volkswagen 'Kubelwagen' staff car.*

Italy. The standard Italian field gun, the 75/27 (75-mm calibre, or internal diameter/27 calibres long), was quite inadequate by modern standards. It was capable of hurling its 14-pound shell 9,000 yards, which was poor enough in itself, but in order to attain this range (or any range over 6,600 yards) it was necessary to dig a pit for the trail in order to obtain the proper elevation and to use a false angle of sight. Additionally, the shell itself had poor fragmentation capabilities.

Otherwise, Italian guns were unspectacular but generally adequate and remarkably dependable. The most-used piece was the 105/28 gun. This was the standard battalion gun and proved valuable in North Africa. Two howitzers, the 100/17 and the 149/13, were common. These were accurate pieces but, like the 105/28 gun, they were hampered by old carriages and long, unwieldy trails which made them unsuitable for mobile warfare.

The most-feared Italian gun was the Ansaldo 75/46 AA gun, a mobile, rapid-fire piece which could be adapted to a number of field roles. Allied tankmen particularly disliked this gun, whose low silhouette, combined with the Italian practice of camouflaging their guns with light grey and dirty white colours, made it virtually invisible at 500 yards.

Japan. The artillery tradition of the Imperial Japanese Army is confined wholly to the modern era, and for that reason Japanese gunners in World War II were not hamstrung, as others undoubtedly were, by conservative attitudes inherited from old wars. This, however, allied to a general lack of experience, had its drawbacks as well as its benefits. For example, Japanese forces in the field were often weak in armour, but on the other hand their anti-tank defences, based upon the indiscriminate use of any guns available, were usually formidable. In fact, the only weapon the Japanese developed specifically for anti-tank work was the Type 1 (1941) 47-mm gun, which was a copy of a German design; where this gun was not in use, it was not uncommon for Allied tanks to encounter field guns sited to cover tank obstacles.

If the Japanese were somewhat unconventional in their use of artillery, they were also quite inept at first. Years of fighting in China against an enemy without adequate artillery had induced among Japanese gunners a naïve lack of concern for customary precautions. Thus in the early actions in the Philippines they fought their guns in the open with a total disregard for concealment, dispersion and camouflage. Their counter-battery work was equally poor. In due course, however, exposure to devastating concentrations from US guns brought about a remarkable improvement, and a few months later they seemed to have re-acquired their old skills.

A favourite Japanese tactic seems to have been to add a fifth, 'ranging' gun to each battery. While the guns of the battery were firing on their target, this gun would obtain data for the next target by firing ranging shots.

After their early successes, the Japanese became plagued by chronic ammunition shortages. While these shortages certainly reduced the overall effectiveness of Japanese artillery, the Allies could not afford to disregard it. In a situation where every shot counted, the Japanese would often obtain range data in a leisurely fashion, creating the impression that they were engaging in harassing fire, and then deluge the target with a brief, destructive concentration.

Japanese guns were, for the most part, modern, tractor-towed types. They included the Type 90 (1930) 75-mm field gun, an excellent long-barrelled weapon with a slotted muzzle-brake and an extreme range of 16,350 yards, and the Type 95 (1935) 75-mm gun, which had been designed to replace the venerable Type 38 (1905) 75-mm gun in the divisional artillery. The older types were still prevalent in quiet areas. The training manual of the Type 31 (1898) 75-mm mountain gun was still being printed as late as 1938; this antique gun, complete with cable and spring recoil system, served in the Pacific during World War II.

Heavier guns included the Type 92 (1932) 105-mm gun, easily recognized by its massive wooden wheels and solid rubber tyres, and the Type 89 (1929) 150-mm gun, a useful model frequently encountered in cave positions. The Type 89 could be broken down into two loads for transport. Among the howitzers were the Type 91 (1931) 105-mm light divisional howitzer, and the Type 96 (1936) 150-mm howitzer, a very modern design.

If there was an area in which the Japanese were weak, it was in their anti-aircraft defence. Their fire-direction and ranging equipment was crude, and their anti-aircraft guns little better. They were usually equipped with light anti-aircraft guns mostly of naval origin–captured or copied Bofors guns and Oerlikon 20-mm aircraft guns. Medium and heavy anti-aircraft fire was provided by an array of naval guns and the Type 88 (1928) 75-mm AA gun, a mobile piece with unimpressive capabilities.

German 15-cm Nebelwerfer 41

SPECIFICATIONS

Weight	1,191 pounds (firing position)
Range	7,723 yards (HE)
	7,546 yards (smoke)
Elevation	+ 5 to + 45 degrees
Traverse	27 degrees
Projectile	15-cm spin-stabilized rocket
Weight of projectile	70 pounds (HE)
	79 pounds (smoke)
Velocity	1,120 fps
Firing mechanism	electrical hand-generator

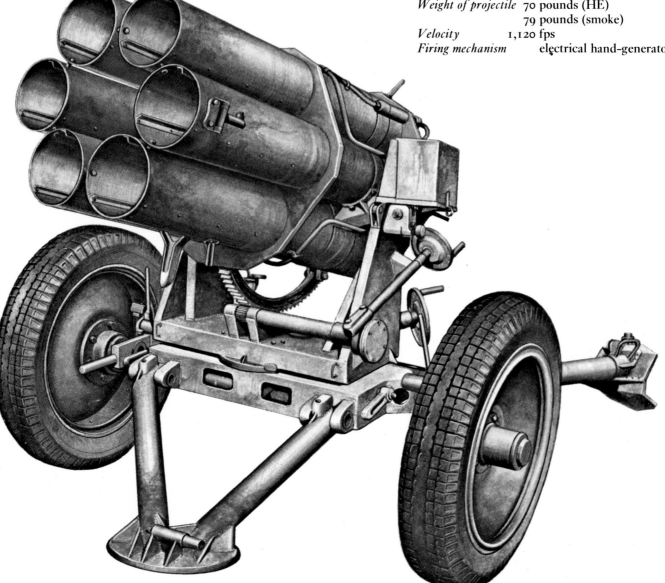

Rocket artillery is probably as old as gunpowder, and rockets were first used on European battlefields as early as 1232. The British Army formed rocket batteries equipped with Sir William Congreve's rockets during the Napoleonic Wars and used them with great success. The United States formed a rocket battery for use in the Mexican War, and by 1860 there were rocket batteries in the British, French, Russian and Austrian armies. Thereafter, rockets fell out of favour with professional military men, probably because of their inaccuracy; according to General Lallemand, a Frenchman, they were 'at best fit to frighten horses'. No rockets were used in World War I, but the experiments of various scientists, notably Dr Robert H. Goddard, coupled with improvements in high explosives, had seemed to point to a day when rockets would once again be extensively used.

During the 1930s extensive experimentation with war rockets and launchers was carried out in Russia and Germany. The Russians developed the Katyusha mobile rocket battery and an air-to-surface AT rocket. German development was extensive in the surface-to-surface category, leading to potent area-fire weapons of the Nebelwerfer type. German self-propelled rocket batteries were usually mounted on half-tracks.

The Nebelwerfer 41 was widely used by the Wehrmacht, beginning in 1942. It could saturate an area with HE, smoke or chemical shells (the latter were not used in combat) and its volume of fire was greatly feared. Nebelwerfers were difficult to conceal in action because, like all rocket weapons, they gave off a heavy back-blast, and each rocket left long, smoky trails along its trajectory.

Anti-Tank Guns in Europe 1940–42

The 'phoney war' on the Western Front ended on 10 May 1940 when the Panzer divisions rolled into France and the Low Countries. In the French campaign German anti-tank gunners played a limited but crucial role. The Flak gunners attached to the Panzer divisions were especially important to the German effort as few German tanks were capable of challenging heavily armoured Allied tanks like the British Matilda or the French Somua.

The story of the German Flakartillerie (Flak= *Flugabwehrkanone* or anti-aircraft gun) intrudes on our narrative about anti-tank guns because the Wehrmacht, partly by design and partly as a matter of expediency, employed AA the under-gunned Panzers could not handle. The Wehrmacht's standard anti-tank gun in 1940, the 37-mm Pak 35/36, was, like nearly every other AT gun then available, ineffective at ranges beyond 500 yards.

On the other hand the Allied anti-tank effort in France is best described in the words of a young French officer, written just before his suicide: 'One cannot send men to fight tanks with rifles'. This was no exaggeration. Most French units were 33–50% below establishment in AT weapons. The British Expeditionary Force was equipped with a superbly designed 2-pounder anti-tank gun, but, like its German counterpart, this gun was not effective beyond short ranges. The best anti-tank gun available to the Allies was the venerable French 75-mm field gun which, of course, was not designed for AT work and was vulnerable to German field artillery when employed in the AT role.

guns in AT roles. Indeed, the standard heavy AA gun of the Flakartillerie – the '88', or 8·8-cm Flak 18 (also 36 and 38) – is primarily remembered as the greatest tank-killer of World War II.

The German experience in the 'rehearsal' provided by the Spanish Civil War (1936–39) had shown that the Flak guns, while engaging in their primary AA role, were frequently called upon for AT work. Thereafter the most-used German AA guns were specifically designed for a dual AA/AT role, and it was a common practice for fully motorized Luftwaffe Flak units to be attached to army units in the field.

The French campaign further reinforced the conviction that the Flak units should play a dual role, for it was in France that the '88' began engaging Allied armour that

As Allied resistance in France crumbled, General Maxime Weygand ordered the French armies to form a defence in depth on a system resembling a checkerboard. The idea behind Weygand's *quadrillage* defence system was to blunt, contain and ultimately destroy the Panzer divisions. The order came too late to have an appreciable effect on operations in France, but the Germans would encounter a sophisticated variation of the *quadrillage* system at Kursk in Russia, where Soviet AT guns would take an incredible toll of German armour.

In the North African campaign of 1940–43 the overall German superiority in weaponry, so evident in Poland and France, had begun to wear thin by 1942. The Germans managed to retain superiority only in the quality of their anti-tank guns. Indeed, the startling string of successes put together by General Erwin Rommel's Afrika Korps (DAK) may be attributed in large measure to Rommel's skilful use of anti-tank guns. At the very heart of Rommel's technique lay the German *Einheit* (unit) system of organization and co-operation of arms. As General von Mellenthin described it:

A German Panzer division was a highly flexible formation of all arms, which always relied on artillery in attack or defence. In contrast, the British regarded the anti-tank gun as a defensive weapon.

(from *Panzer Battles*, by General F. W. von Mellenthin)

The Panzers were, quite literally, never alone. The artillery attached to a Panzer division kept pace with it even on sustained offensives. The British cruiser tanks, on the other hand, operated somewhat like the heavy cavalry

draw, luring the British tanks forward to be smashed by the waiting Flak and AT guns.

The British were further handicapped in North Africa because the 2-pounder was the only anti-tank gun they systematically used until the introduction in 1942 of the 6-pounder (57-mm) AT gun. A conservative obstinacy concerning the proper role of the 3·7-inch AA gun, a weapon superior to the German '88' in almost every respect, prevented its use in the AT role.

The standard German anti-tank gun in North Africa was the 50-mm Pak 38. This weapon had replaced the obsolete Pak 35/36 very early in the campaign. In 1942 large numbers of captured Russian field guns, mostly converted 76-mm Pak 36s, began to appear in the anti-tank armoury of the DAK. The superiority of these weapons to the British 2-pounder, combined with the inability of the

OPPOSITE *The crew of a German Pak 40 AT gun brings light-machine-gun fire to bear on a group of Russian huts and outbuildings.*
RIGHT *Voronezh, Russia. A German '88' crew observes the effect of its fire.*
BELOW *A Soviet 76-mm AT gun M-1942. This light and mobile gun was the standard divisional AT gun of the Soviet armies. With high-velocity armour-piercing ammunition it attained an exceptional muzzle velocity of 3,167 fps. The gun weighed one ton and had a maximum range of 14,545 yards.*

brigades of the Napoleonic Wars. They would charge forward, far outstripping their artillery and infantry supports. In the face of this charge, the Panzers would with-

British field artillery—good though it was—to act in co-operation with its tank forces, made North Africa a graveyard for Allied tanks.

Throughout those years the gun-armour race ground on. Eventually, even bigger guns and more powerful projectiles with greater armour-piercing capabilities were introduced. Anti-tank guns were especially critical on the Eastern Front. The Russians found that their 76-mm divisional gun M-1942 was unable to deal with heavy German tanks and they eventually settled on the 100-mm M-1944 for this role. The Germans progressed from the 75-mm Pak 40 (introduced for service in late 1942) to the 128-mm Pak 44. The biggest British anti-tank gun was the 17-pounder Mark 1. This gun arrived in Tunisia just in time to deal with the new German heavy tank, the Tiger.

German Sd Kfz 138 Marder III

This German SP (self-propelled) gun is typical of the SP guns of World War II. A tank chassis (in this case the Czech 38t Praga) was utilized as a weapons carrier, and a thinly armoured superstructure, incorporating the fighting compartment, was built over it. These were stop-gap measures, designed to meet demand.

Such guns, in co-operation with motorized infantry (Panzergrenadiers in the German Army) acted with armoured divisions in wide-ranging operations, providing the fire support and staying power that armour lacked. Some, like the vehicle shown here, were Panzerjägers (tank-hunters) and fulfilled the same role in the motorized unit as the anti-tank gun in conventional units.

The Marder III began to appear in March 1942. The first production models were equipped with the Russian 76·2-mm field gun, but one year later a much-improved version with the 75-mm Pak 40/3 was put into production. The one great fault of the Marder III was its open fighting compartment which exposed the crew to blast and splinters from enemy HE fire. By May 1944 production of the Marder was terminated, and the Jagdpanzer 38 Hetzer, which had a fully enclosed fighting compartment, began to take its place in front-line units.

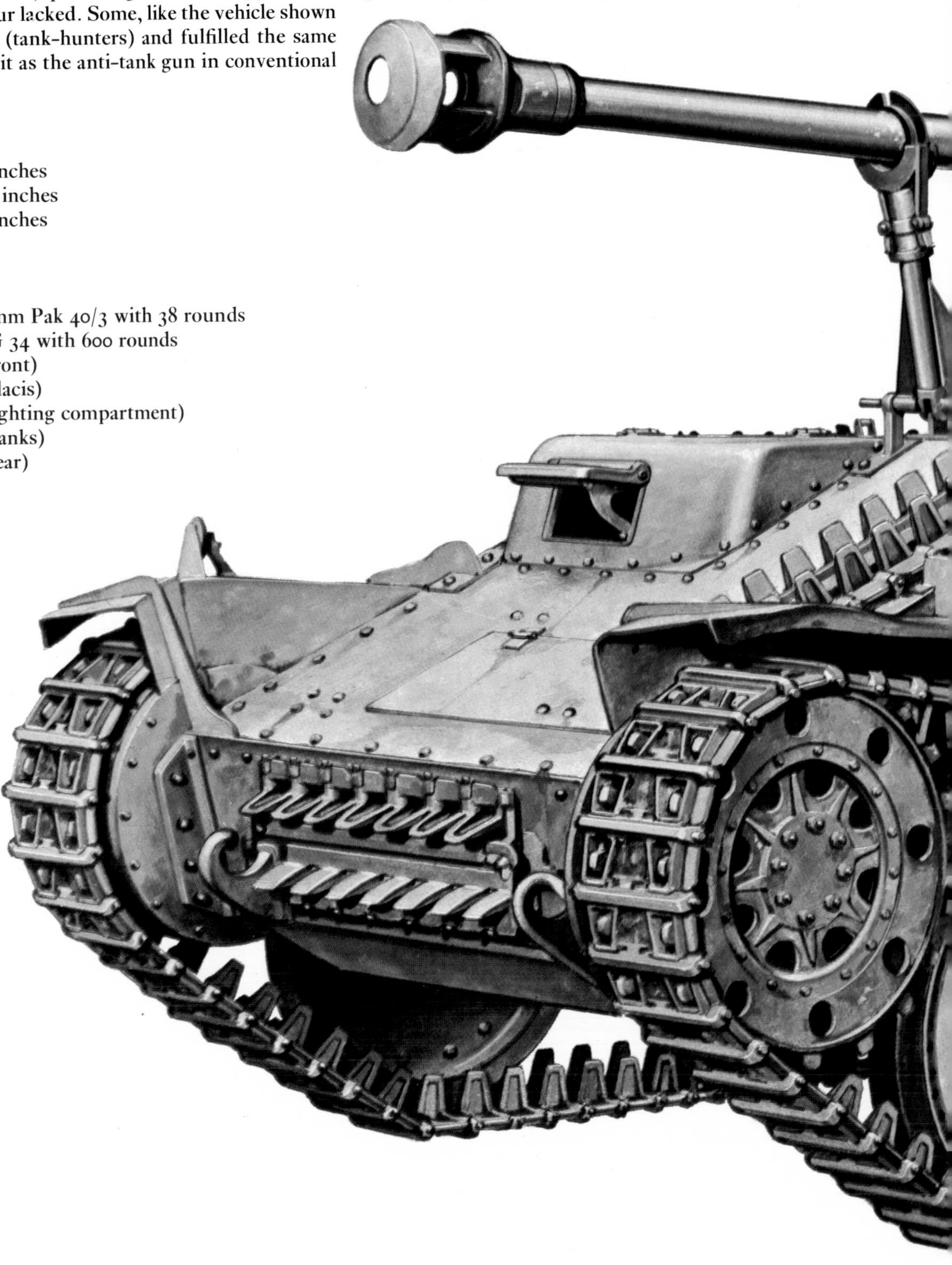

SPECIFICATIONS

Length	15 feet 6 inches
Width	7 feet 10 inches
Height	8 feet 4 inches
Weight	10·8 tons
Speed	28 mph
Range	112 miles
Armament	1 × 75-mm Pak 40/3 with 38 rounds
	1 × MG 34 with 600 rounds
Armour	15 mm (front)
	11 mm (glacis)
	10 mm (fighting compartment)
	10 mm (flanks)
	10 mm (rear)
Crew	4

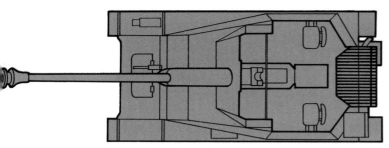

LEFT *This top view of the Marder III highlights its chief drawback as a combat vehicle, namely the lack of protection for the crew in the gun's fighting compartment. This shortcoming was rectified in the later SP guns of World War II.*
BELOW *The large view shows the two basic elements of the Marder III – the Czech 38t tank chassis and the armoured superstructure housing the main armament that was built onto it. Note also the spare sections of track fixed to the vehicle.*

'Gustav' at Sebastopol

The largest guns ever built were two 80-cm rail guns made by Krupp to bombard the Maginot Line. These Brobdingnagian pieces were nicknamed 'Gustav' and 'Dora'. Only Gustav saw action, being used at Sebastopol in 1942 and at Warsaw in 1944. Field Marshal Erich von Manstein, who commanded the German Eleventh Army in the operations against Sebastopol, described Gustav as:

> A miracle of technical achievement. The barrel must have been 90 feet long and the carriage as high as a two-storey house. Sixty trains had been required to bring it into position along a railway specially laid for the purpose. Two anti-aircraft regiments had to be constantly in attendance.

> (from *Lost Victories*, by Erich von Manstein)

Gustav's capabilities were equally impressive. One of its seven-ton concrete-piercing shells crashed through 90 feet of hard rock and destroyed a Russian ammunition dump near Severnaya Bay. But, despite its awesome credentials, Gustav was something of a white elephant. As von Manstein expressed it: 'The effectiveness of the cannon bore no real relation to all the effort and expense that had gone into making it' (*Lost Victories*).

Joining Gustav in the task of battering Sebastopol into submission were two mammoth 60-cm 'Karl' SP howitzers and numerous other heavy guns. Altogether, von Manstein's Eleventh Army marshalled 208 batteries along a 22-mile front. This was the greatest German artillery concentration of the war. Much of the credit for the German conquest of the Crimea in 1942 must in fact be given to the artillery, for von Manstein's army was operating almost the whole time without armour.

ABOVE *The shattered Soviet turreted battery 'Maxim Gorki', near Sebastopol in the Crimea. The battery capitulated after sapper operations and a point-blank duel with German artillery.*
OPPOSITE *'Gustav', the giant 80-cm rail gun originally built by Krupp to bombard the Maginot Line.*
RIGHT *Another German mammoth, here seen in the 22-mile artillery front assembled by von Manstein to bombard Sebastopol.*

The Anti-Tank War Phase 2

The story of the anti-tank gun inevitably leads from the gun-armour race to the development of sophisticated systems of anti-tank defences. Although there had been little optimism among military men at the ability of guns to stop tanks, far-sighted theorists like Generals J.F.C. Fuller and S.L.A. Marshall had advocated the construction of elaborate, co-operative defence systems, and Rommel had shown the way with his tank-proof localities in the Western Desert.

The most complex application of this principle was the defence system created by the Russian armies in the Kursk salient in 1943. At Kursk the Russians held a mammoth salient projecting into the lines of von Kluge's Army Group Centre. Against it the Germans prepared a strike force of their finest Panzer and infantry divisions. But because of the activities of the Swiss master-spy 'Lucy', the Russians were well aware of the Germans' intentions and had adequately prepared to meet the attack.

ABOVE *A German 75/55-mm AT gun with tapered bore. The last AT gun put into service by the German Army in World War II, it employed the highly successful Gerlich or coned-bore principle. The bore tapered from 75 mm at the breech to 55 mm at the muzzle. An extremely high muzzle velocity of 4,000 fps (estimated) could be attained with this coned bore and a flanged tungsten carbide projectile. The shot could penetrate 5 inches of armour at 1,500 yards.*
BELOW *Action on the Eastern Front: a German 21-cm gun fires at the Russian defences.*

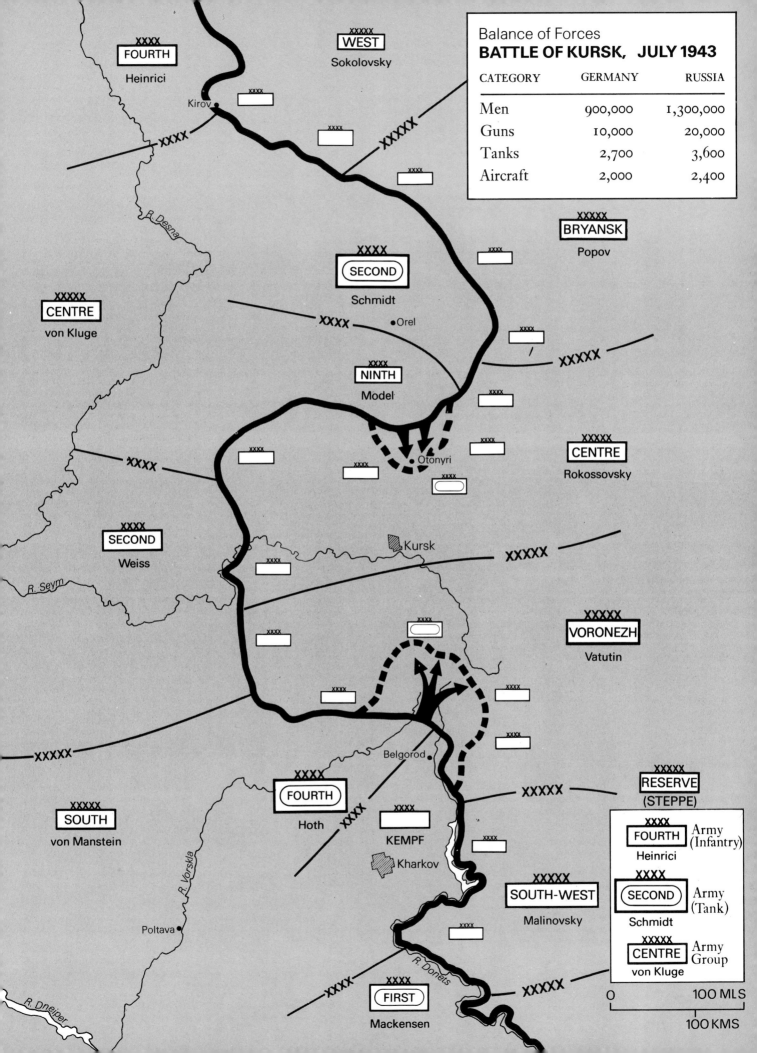

XXXX
FOURTH
Heinrici

XXXXX
WEST
Sokolovsky

Kirov

XXXX

XXXXX

XXXX

R. Desna

XXXX
SECOND
Schmidt

Orel

XXXX

XXXXX
BRYANSK
Popov

XXXXX
CENTRE
von Kluge

XXXX

XXXX
NINTH
Model

XXXX

XXXX

XXXX

XXXX
Otonyri

XXXXX
CENTRE
Rokossovsky

XXXX

XXXX

XXXX
SECOND
Weiss

R. Seym

Kursk

XXXXX

XXXX

XXXX

XXXXX
VORONEZH
Vatutin

XXXX

XXXX

XXXX

XXXXX

XXXXX

Belgorod

XXXXX
RESERVE
(STEPPE)

XXXX
FOURTH
Hoth

XXXX

XXXX
KEMPF

XXXXX
SOUTH
von Manstein

R. Vorskla

Kharkov

XXXXX
SOUTH-WEST
Malinovsky

Poltava

XXXX

R. Donets

XXXX

XXXX
FIRST
Mackensen

R. Dnieper

XXXXX

Balance of Forces **BATTLE OF KURSK, JULY 1943**		
CATEGORY	GERMANY	RUSSIA
Men	900,000	1,300,000
Guns	10,000	20,000
Tanks	2,700	3,600
Aircraft	2,000	2,400

XXXX
FOURTH   Army (Infantry)
Heinrici

XXXX
SECOND   Army (Tank)
Schmidt

XXXXX
CENTRE   Army Group
von Kluge

0   100 MLS

100 KMS

Along the perimeter of the salient the Russians constructed several parallel lines of defence. These lines were protected by massive minefield belts which were arranged with the additional object of channelling the Panzers towards innumerable clusters of anti-tank guns. The anti-tank guns were formed in groups of 10 guns (called 'Pak-fronts' by the Germans), which were instructed to hold their fire until the target presented a flank shot. The idea was to allow penetration of the front lines and then, by a process of peeling away the enemy's flank armour, break up the impetus of the attack. The reserve consisted of artillery and Koniev's Fifth Tank Army. Altogether, the Kursk salient held 20,000 guns (6,000 in the Pak-fronts) and 920 Katyusha rocket-launchers.

The German plan of attack called for a pincer movement against the northern and southern flanks of the salient. Model's Ninth Army would strike the northern face from the direction of Orel, while Hoth's Fourth Panzer Army would strike the southern face. The build-up for the attack took months to complete and eventually involved drawing the bulk of German armour on the Eastern Front into the area around Kursk (75% of the strength of the entire German Army was then in Russia). The concentration of guns and tanks on the attack fronts was dense even by German standards. Model's front, the strongest, averaged 60–80 tanks and 110–130 guns per mile of front.

Tactically, the Germans formed their tanks in arrowhead-like formations known as the Panzer *Keil*, or wedge. In this formation heavily armoured tanks and assault guns such as the Tiger and the Ferdinand took the lead, while medium tanks, mostly Panthers and Mark IVs, followed in echelon behind.

On 5 July 1943 the Battle of Kursk opened. What followed has been described as the greatest tank battle in history, but that familiar and laconic description should not be allowed to obscure the fact that Kursk was won largely by the gunners of the Russian Pak-fronts. At first there was no stopping the mammoth Ferdinands, which soon outstripped the smaller tanks, but the Russian anti-tank guns slowed, stopped or disorganized most of the German thrusts, and then flamethrower crews dealt one by one with the isolated Ferdinands. On 12 July Koniev's tanks struck the flank of the floundering German advance near Prokhorovka, and the outcome was settled.

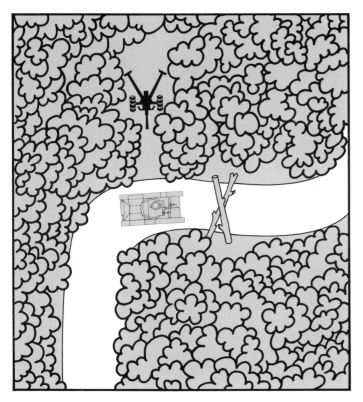

Kursk was one of the truly decisive battles in world history. German losses were immense and irreplaceable. Of the total of some 2,700 tanks Model and Hoth had hurled against the salient, over 90 per cent were left on the field of battle. The effort broke the back of Hitler's Panzer armies, and the Russians took over the initiative in the Ukraine.

From there the war on the Eastern Front became, from the German side, an almost continuous rearguard action lasting nearly two years as the Russians pushed westwards through Poland to the outskirts of Berlin. On 25 April 1945 they opened up on the inner suburbs of Hitler's capital with a final barrage of 2,000,000 shells. Within a fortnight the war in the West was over.

LEFT *Scenario for a tank ambush: the tank turns the bend in the road and is halted by the road block; in this position it presents a maximum target to the camouflaged AT gun.*
OPPOSITE, BELOW *A Soviet fully tracked carriage with a 203-mm howitzer M-1931. This was the standard heavy howitzer in service with the Soviet armies, the carriage being especially useful in difficult terrain. It had a range of 19,700 yards.*
BELOW *Soviet Katyusha rocket teams in the battle for Berlin.*

Self-Propelled Guns

There are two main types of self-propelled (SP) guns: firstly, there are the heavily armoured assault guns and tank destroyers; secondly, the lightly armoured support guns. SP guns fulfil the same functions as their horse- and tractor-drawn counterparts but, of course, enjoy the advantages of independent mobility.

SP guns saw limited action during World War I. Early models were slow and, for the most part, lacked armour protection for their crews. During World War II the SP gun really came of age. Each of the belligerents fielded great numbers of them, most notably Germany, which by the end of the war had more Panzerjägers (self-propelled anti-tank guns, literally 'tank-hunters') than tanks.

Another type of SP gun appeared during the war. This was the assault gun. The first assault guns used in battle were a small number of German Sturmgeschütz IIIs armed with the short 75-mm Stu.K L/24; these were used in the Ardennes sector during the invasion of France in 1940. The experiment was a success, and the Germans eventually built over 10,500 Sturmgeschütz-type assault guns during the war, while their Italian allies produced an excellent version, the Semovente M-40 and M-41 mounting the DA 75/18 gun. Another group of assault guns was built specifically for attacking fortifications or for use in street fighting. These,

of course, were larger and more heavily armoured and they mounted bigger guns. Among them were the box-like Brummbär (Growler) assault howitzer and the Sturmtiger, which mounted the 38-cm RW-61 rocket mortar.

The Soviet Union built its first unarmoured SP gun in 1932, and during World War II developed an entire family of SP assault and support guns built around the chassis of their successful T-34 medium and JS heavy tanks. The SU-76 support gun mounted the 76-mm M-1942 divisional gun and was originally developed as a tank destroyer; but it was unsuccessful in that role and finished the war as the standard Soviet SP support gun. The first heavily armoured Soviet assault gun was the SU-85, which appeared in the

LEFT *During the takeover of Berlin, a column of Soviet JSU-152a assault guns parks at the side of the road.*
TOP *A German Stu.G III Ausf.D assault gun advances with infantry support on Russian positions near Voronezh in 1943.*
ABOVE *An Italian Ansaldo 90/53 SP gun M-1941 captured in Sicily.*

battles in the Ukraine in 1944. It mounted the 85-mm AA gun on the T-34 chassis. The SU-85 was followed by the SU-100, which mounted the powerful 100-mm. M-1944 field gun; the JSU-122 mounting the 122-mm gun A-195, and the JSU-152 mounting the 152-mm gun-howitzer M-1937.

During the great Soviet offensives of 1944–45 the assault guns were well to the front. Each assault-gun battery had orders to follow the infantry or armour it was supporting by no more than 400 yards. Their fire was used to engage enemy tanks and artillery and to destroy strongpoints. Most of these assault guns remained in service in the decade following the war, not only with Soviet and Eastern European armies but also in the Middle East.

The appearance of seemingly unlimited numbers of Russian tanks and assault guns in the last years of the war forced the Germans to resort to the cheap expedient of the Panzerjäger. Early German tank-hunters had been built with open fighting compartments, but there were obvious drawbacks associated with this mode of construction. Usually they had to wait for the enemy to come to them and, after their first shots, were then subjected to massive retaliatory fire. The second generation of tank-hunters was therefore built with a closed and heavily armoured fighting compartment to protect the crew. Among the vehicles in this class were the Hetzer, the Jagdpanther, the Jagdtiger and the redoubtable Ferdinand.

Assault guns and tank-hunters were the most prevalent form of SP artillery on the Eastern Front, but the Western Allies favoured the SP support gun. The need for SP support guns had become evident in North Africa. At first, the Lee-Grant tank was used in this role, firing its short 75-mm sponson gun from hull- and turret-down positions. Later, the appearance of the M-7 Priest gave the Allies an excellent SP gun comparable to the German Wespe, which mounted the 10·5-cm L/28. Another favoured type was the M-10 tank destroyer. The first British SP field-gun was the Sexton, which mounted the 25-pounder. The Sexton was not a successful type, however, since its high silhouette made concealment difficult.

In the course of the war several larger guns were mounted on tank chassis, and the trend in artillery development since that time has been to seek increased mobility through improved SP mounts. Today, all but the largest guns are mounted on purpose-built SP mounts.

BELOW *A US M-10 tank destroyer in action against a German pillbox near Echternach, Luxembourg, in 1945.*
OPPOSITE, ABOVE *A German Jagdpanther, one of the second generation of German tank-hunters developed in wartime. This vehicle was knocked out in March 1945 by a US tank destroyer.*
OPPOSITE, BELOW *The German Sturmtiger, a massive 70-ton assault vehicle designed partly for a street-fighting role. Its main armament was the RW-61 rocket launcher; the rocket's exhaust gases escaped through the circular vents at the muzzle.*

Anti-Aircraft Guns

Anti-aircraft artillery had performed in a satisfactory, albeit clumsy, manner in World War I, and for some years after 1918 there seemed to be little need to improve on the capabilities of existing AA guns. Suddenly, in the mid-1930s, aircraft development accelerated, and by the time of the Spanish Civil War (1936–39) it was clear that aircraft would take a major role in any future conflict.

Following the war in Spain ordnance experts in the United States and Great Britain worked to develop AA guns and complex new detection and aiming devices capable of putting up a strong defence against fast attack aircraft and high-flying bombers. Top priority was given to the development of a light, Quick-Firing AA gun with sufficient hitting power to bring down dive-bombers and ground-attack fighters such as the German Stukas. Initial attempts to develop light cannon for this role did not meet with much success. The US Army, for example, adapted its 37-mm AT gun for this purpose, but the gun was found to be inaccurate, weak in hitting power, in fact totally unsuited for the role the experts had thrust upon it. Eventually, nearly all the major combatant nations in World War II settled on the Bofors 40-mm AA gun (or copies or derivatives of it) as their standard light flak weapon.

The Bofors 40-mm gun was developed in Sweden in the early 1930s. It first proved its worth against low-level attacks in the Battle of Britain and eventually also it was useful as an assault gun against ground targets. What made the Bofors especially deadly in either role was its high cyclic rate of fire. It was capable of firing two rounds per second over a slant range of four miles. The shells were fed into the loading tray in four-round clips and automatically rammed into the firing chamber.

Anti-aircraft defence against high-flying bombers was a much simpler proposition. In this category, at least, there was no need for the ordnance experts to adapt or develop in haste. Guns capable of bringing down a strategic bomber had been in existence since World War I; even so, such guns were becoming outmoded by 1939 even if they were not quite obsolescent.

The German 88-mm Flak 18, which made its début in the Spanish Civil War, was the first of a new generation of heavy AA guns. The appearance of the '88' caused quite a stir, because it was far superior to the older mobile AA guns.

BELOW *A flying bomb is near, the alert has been sounded and these British crews run to man their Bofors AA guns.*
OPPOSITE, ABOVE *A Bofors crew at action stations on one of the island forts sited off the coast of Britain.*
OPPOSITE, BELOW *German AA gunners manning a 37-mm Flak 36 AA gun in the Caucasus. As the Russians began to gain air supremacy in 1942, the Flakartillerie's role grew critical.*

Soon, however, other nations produced AA guns comparable to the '88' in service performance. Great Britain's 3·7-inch Mark I was ready for service in 1939 but was not used extensively until the North African campaign. Until then the 3-inch 20-cwt gun, of World War I vintage, was used by British and Commonwealth units. The last development of the 3·7-inch gun, the Mark 6, was in service at the war's end; this was a very superior piece which remained standard until it was replaced by surface-to-air missiles. A US gun, the 90-mm M-2, was introduced for service in 1942; it could fire 20–25 rounds per minute to a height of nine miles. All these new-generation guns were also effective in the anti-tank role, although the British and American guns were used less often for this purpose.

The heaviest mobile AA gun produced during the war was the US 120-mm M-1. This weapon, known as the 'Stratosphere Gun', was designed specifically to counter an anticipated high-level German bombing raid on the USA. It had a vertical range of 12 miles (20,000 feet higher than any other mobile AA gun).

Notable improvements were made during the pre-war years in AA fire-control systems and in the use of radio (radar) directors. The first electrical fire-control systems

On a Normandy beachhead on D-Day, the crew of a US 90-mm AA gun fires on hostile targets.

were developed after World War I, but truly efficient systems were not produced before the 1930s. These systems rapidly supplanted plotting boards and mechanical fire-control equipment, which were slow, cumbersome and, of course, plagued by the element of human error.

The new electrical fire-control apparatus collected data from the tracker and range-finder and transmitted it continuously to a computer which instantly calculated the proper setting for the shell's time fuse and the correct direction and elevation for gun-laying. The computer also made instantaneous corrections for wind, weather and barometric conditions. The data was then transmitted to the gun and fuse-setter; a great deal of time was saved and the possibility of human error was eliminated from that part of the operation.

The next important improvement was in the field of radar directors. The British and Americans developed radar 'early-warning' systems almost simultaneously in 1936; within a year, the US Army successfully demonstrated a radar detector and director system at the Signal Corps laboratories in Fort Monmouth, New Jersey. When radar detection and direction systems were combined with electrical fire-control and (later) the VT fuse, AA guns became very efficient indeed. In the course of World War II the USA, Great Britain and Germany all used sophisticated detection and direction systems for their AA guns.

VT Fuse

On 16 December 1944 the German counter-offensive (the Battle of the Bulge) was in full stride in the Ardennes. Harsh weather, fog and surprise had aided the advance. Suddenly, German troops were caught in the open by an intense, surprisingly lethal artillery concentration. Road columns of infantry and highway intersections were engulfed in flame and shell fragments. Each shell burst above the ground at precisely the height from which its fragments would do the most damage. There had been no ranging shots and, therefore, no warning. The fog, traditionally a shield behind which troops could be moved in some safety, had been no protection. As confusion and consternation spread among the German troops, their great counter-offensive ground to a halt.

This was the first instance of the use of a truly revolutionary ordnance development— the VT fuse–against a ground target. Its use was credited with stopping the Germans in the Ardennes and, ultimately, helping to win the Battle of the Bulge. General Patton later commented: 'The new shell with the "funny fuse" is devastating. . . . I think that when all armies get this fuse, we will have to devise some new method of warfare'.

The VT fuse had been developed by a team of American researchers led by Dr Vannevar Bush. Each VT fuse incorporated a tiny radio receiving and transmitting set. The fuse could detonate the shell at any height or distance from the target based upon the radar impulses the fuse received during the flight of the shell. As opposed to conventional time fuses, which were pre-set before firing, the VT fuse responded to the proximity of the target, detonating its shell when it detected that it was within lethal distance.

The devastating potential of the new fuse was well understood. At first, its use was limited to AA work, where there was no possibility of the enemy recovering a 'dud' and copying the fuse. Its effectiveness was established beyond question in the Pacific and in countering the V-1 rocket attacks on London. Shells fitted with VT fuses hit 79% of the rockets launched against London.

Later, as we have seen, the VT fuse was issued for land use, and is credited with increasing the effectiveness of artillery by a factor of 10 times over shells fitted with conventional time fuses.

The Germans failed to produce a satisfactory proximity fuse in time, although they were working at it up to the end of the war. This is revealed, for example, by the fact that their air-to-air rockets were equipped with recesses to take the fuse as and when it became available.

A demonstration of the VT fuse with a 155-mm shell. Note the dust rising where shell splinters have penetrated the roofs.

US 75-mm Recoilless Rifle M-20

SPECIFICATIONS

Calibre	75 mm (2·95 inches)
Maximum range	7,000 yards (HEAT)
	6,955 yards (HE or smoke)
Length of gun tube	64·8 inches
Length of piece	82 inches
Elevation	−27 to +65 degrees
Traverse	360 degrees
Weight	114·5 pounds (with sight bracket)
	158 pounds (including mount)
Muzzle velocity	1,000 fps (HEAT)
Weight of projectile	14·6 pounds
Weight of propellant	2·5 pounds
Breech-block operation	interrupted screw

The side view shows the gun mounted on its tripod ready for action. Weighing 114·5 pounds, this infantry-portable weapon was at its best against relatively fixed targets such as tanks, pillboxes and machine-gun nests.

The first recoilless (RCL) gun was the Davis Gun (*c*. 1910). This gun, which was employed to a limited extent in World War I, utilized a principle of physics to do away with the problem of recoil. The Davis Gun had two diametrically opposing barrels sharing a common powder chamber. Two projectiles of equal weight were loaded into the gun. When the gun was fired there was no recoil as the two projectiles moved down the opposing barrels at equal speed and exerted equal but opposite recoil stress on the gun. The 'second' projectile, or countershot, consisted of a mixture of grease and small shot and was dispersed on leaving the rear barrel.

Although the advantages of the Davis Gun were manifest, the end of the war also brought an end to its brief career. The next stage was to use, in place of the latter's countershot, a stream of high-velocity gas. During World War II the Germans were the first to field recoilless guns, followed closely by British and US models.

The US recoilless rifles of the Kromuskit family are fairly typical of modern recoilless weapons. Named after their inventors, Kroger and Musser, two such rifles were developed during World War II—a 57-mm model and one of 75-mm—and both were used with great success in the Pacific and European theatres as light infantry-support weapons. The 75-mm recoilless rifle was especially valuable to infantry and airborne units advancing without artillery support who were held up by enemy strongpoints. The gun's light weight enabled it to accompany

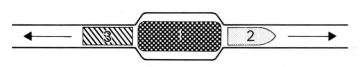

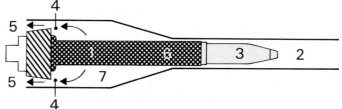

Davis Gun—the RCL pioneer

The first recoilless gun featured two opposite-facing barrels sharing a common powder chamber. The projectile occupied one barrel and a countershot of equal weight the other. On firing, they exerted an equal recoil stress and so cancelled each other out.

1 Cartridge
2 Projectile
3 Countershot

Cross-section of RCL

This cross-section through a hypothetical recoilless rifle illustrates the following key principles and components:
1 Many recoilless rifles fire fixed ammunition with a perforated cartridge case. The case is so designed to allow gases to escape to the rear of the piece through a venturi 'throat' after a low pressure has been reached.
2 Rifled bore. The size of the bore is equal to the size of the throats.
3 Standard projectile. This has a pre-engraved rifled band and a standard fuse.
4 Throat, the passage through which gases escape to the rear of the gun.
5 Venturi, the rear opening characteristic of recoilless guns.
6 Charge. Recoilless guns are low-efficiency weapons. Their powder charge has to be comparatively large to achieve a muzzle velocity comparable, though lower, to that of howitzers of the same calibre.
7 Powder chamber. This is abnormally large in weapons of the Kromuskit family.

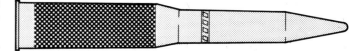

Above is a complete round of HEAT (High Explosive Anti-Tank) ammunition for the 75-mm recoilless rifle; rounds were made with perforated cases to permit propellant gases to escape through the exhaust ports at the rear of the piece.

infantry in the advance, and its accuracy gained it a considerable reputation as a tank-killer.

RCL weapons have certain important disadvantages, however. The foremost is the pronounced back-blast which can endanger a careless crew (the crews of German 7·5-cm RCLs had to wear specially designed ear protectors) and makes concealing the weapon from enemy observation difficult.

Since World War II the Kromuskit RCLs have been replaced by weapons with larger calibres. Today's RCLs have ·50-calibre spotting rifles attached to the tube: these fire tracer bullets for ranging. RCLs were particularly helpful in Korea, where difficult terrain often prevented the artillery from fighting in the front lines.

The War in the Pacific

Operations in the Pacific theatre against the Japanese presented Allied gunners with an altogether different set of problems to those facing their comrades in Europe and Africa. This was largely because Japan was weak industrially and in resources. Two important consequences were that Japanese tanks never became a decisive factor and Allied air supremacy was never seriously challenged (anti-tank and anti-aircraft actions were in fact comparatively rare). Also, in the jungle warfare which characterized most of the campaigns in East Asia and the Pacific, the Japanese were usually on the defensive and almost invariably without air, naval or armoured support. Under these circumstances, artillery became a major element in their defensive systems.

The problems usually associated with campaigning in the Pacific and East Asia created hardships on both sides, but the Allies were better prepared to meet them. Firstly, there was the environment itself, which was generally forbidding and inhospitable; then there were numerous logistical problems, compounded by long distances and the undeveloped nature of the terrain, which further hampered

The 14-inch guns of Fort Drum, the 'concrete battleship', reply to the savage bombardment of the invading Japanese. In the Manila Bay area gigantic artillery duels were fought between 6 February 1942, when the Japanese opened fire from Cavite, and 6 May, when the island forts surrendered. Unfortunately for the Allies, the forts were built to repel a naval invasion, and were overly vulnerable to a land attack.

operations. Nevertheless, Allied artillerymen were usually well supplied with whatever they needed and could afford to expend ammunition lavishly, whereas their Japanese counterparts were significantly less well supplied and had to make every shot count. Another basic problem for the Japanese was their severe shortage of raw industrial chemicals, especially aromatics such as toluene (a basic ingredient of TNT), while the coal-tar industry of the Home Islands was wholly inadequate. As a result Japan could never produce enough explosives to supply her forces in the field.

Still, the Japanese were confident. The 'China Incident', as they called the long war begun with China in 1931, had

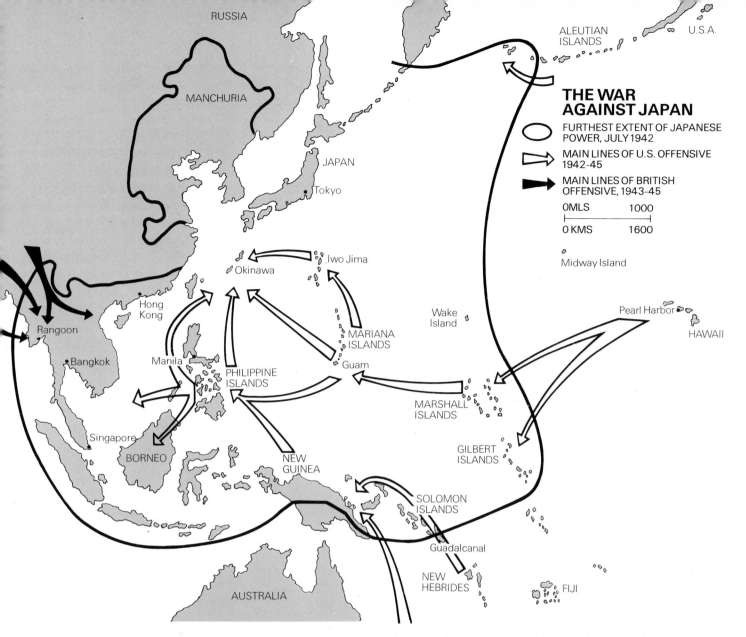

in its early stages proved a heady experience, not least for the gunners. But in the course of that war Japanese gunners had developed bad field habits, and so when they entered the Pacific campaigns they tended to site their guns without sufficient care, paying little regard to cover or camouflage. A border incident with the Russians in Mongolia in 1939 led to the Battle of Khalkin Gol, in which the Japanese were humiliated by a Russian force deploying greatly superior armour and artillery forces. Khalkin Gol produced no great re-thinking of artillery tactics, however, and the Japanese missed a chance to prepare for their next great encounter with the West.

Following the attack on Pearl Harbor in December 1941, the Japanese struck quickly at the great bases of the Allies in East Asia and the Philippines. The battles fought at Singapore and in the Manila Bay area were the last instances in the war in which the Japanese massed their guns to achieve artillery superiority. Singapore fell to General Yamashita's daring amphibious assault backed by 440 guns. The assault came at night, and British Empire artillery

which might have stopped it failed to do so largely because of poor communications.

In the Manila Bay area there were titanic artillery duels between the guns of the island forts (Corregidor and Forts Frank, Hughes and Drum) and Japanese guns on the main-land at Cavite and Bataan. The duels began on 6 February 1942 after the Japanese had secured suitable positions on the Cavite shore. Eventually, the Japanese managed to emplace over 800 guns, including some of 240-mm calibre, and the bombardment rose to peaks of almost incredible intensity.

On 29 April the Japanese commemorated the Emperor's birthday with a tremendous day-long bombardment. Over 10,000 shells devastated Corregidor. Then, on 4 May, over 16,000 shells were directed at 'The Rock', destroying the few guns which remained capable of reply. On the same day Fort Drum, the 'concrete battleship', took 1,000 hits.

Two days later the island forts surrendered before the incessant artillery bombardment. During the siege US counter-battery fire had been fierce but generally in-

113

Japanese Island Defences

In their struggle to retain the Pacific islands which they had themselves taken with little difficulty, the Japanese showed all the near-inhuman hardness characteristic of the Emperor's do-or-die army. On the defensive almost unceasingly for the last three years of the war, the island garrisons emplaced and concealed their artillery with immense thoroughness. They planted new trees and gardens and even built dummy huts mounted on rails to disguise the presence of their larger cannon. For the soldiers manning these gun sites retreat was unthinkable, and the invading Allies had to destroy each position with grenades, guns and flamethrowers.

The beach diagram shows a typical Japanese defensive layout. As they approached the beach, invading forces were shelled and machine-gunned from emplacements at the back of the beach (in the slit trenches shown) and from others higher up in the jungle beyond. Under this steady fire the men in the landing craft had to negotiate a further deadly blend of natural and man-made hazards. These began with the jagged banks of coral surrounding the island. Once inside the lagoon, the invaders' way was strewn with posts and other obstacles; anti-boat mines lay near the shore-line. Lastly came the box mines, concealed with their sensitive trip wires beneath the sand.

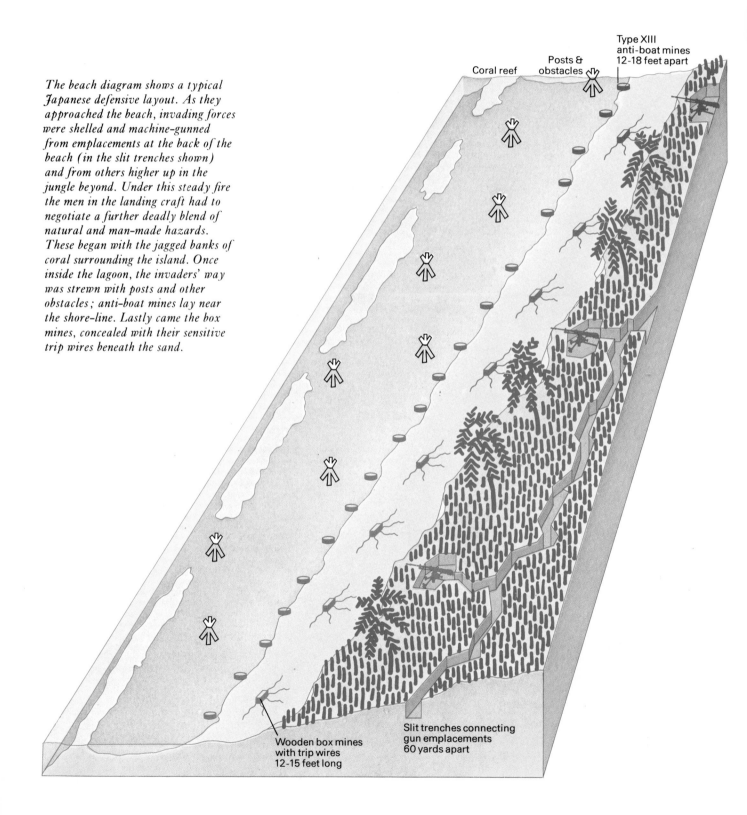

Coral reef

Posts & obstacles

Type XIII anti-boat mines 12-18 feet apart

Wooden box mines with trip wires 12-15 feet long

Slit trenches connecting gun emplacements 60 yards apart

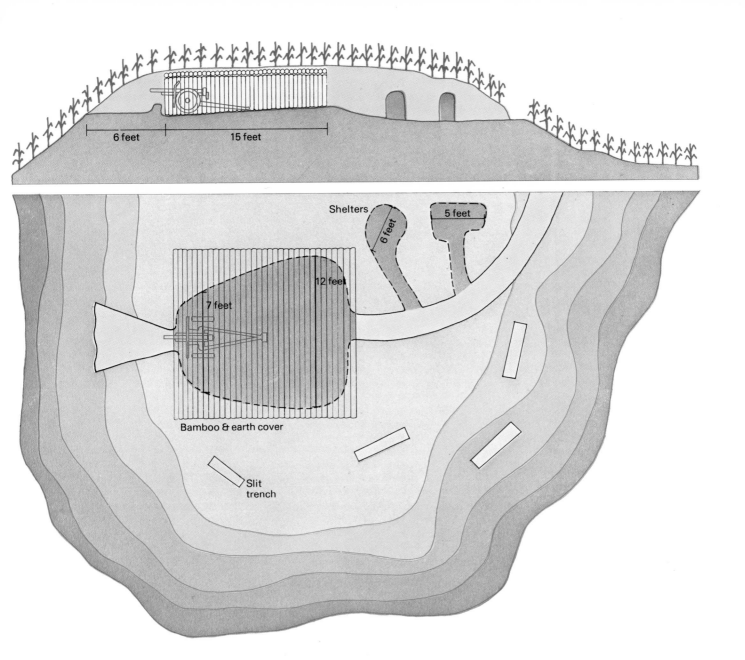

6 feet

15 feet

Shelters

6 feet

5 feet

12 feet

7 feet

Bamboo & earth cover

Slit
trench

ABOVE *Featured here is a typical Japanese hill emplacement. The gun is sited in a hollowed-out cave some 7 feet wide at the front broadening to 12 feet at the rear. The roof consists of bamboo logs and earth; above it a thick cover of trees makes the position virtually undetectable from the air. To the rear of the gun an exit passage with sleeping bays opens onto the reverse slope of the hill. The site is hedged about with slit trenches from which the infantry can bring small-arms fire to bear on the enemy.*

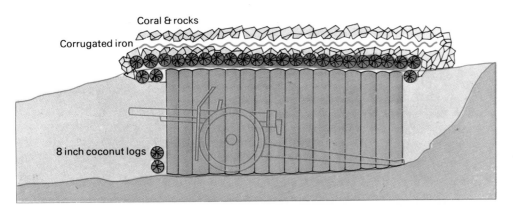

Coral & rocks

Corrugated iron

8 inch coconut logs

LEFT *In the smaller illustration the gun has been concealed in a dug-out of the kind usually found in the vicinity of a beach. Here the local coral is used together with a sheet of corrugated iron and a row of coconut logs to give cover and concealment from the air. (The logs forming the roof rest on ledges not shown in this view.) The side walls of the dug-out are also made of coconut logs.*

effective. The gunners had been impeded by the fact that the Manila Bay forts, like the fortress at Singapore, had been designed to repel a hostile fleet, and were vulnerable to land or air attack. Most of the ammunition for the big guns and mortars was armour-piercing, and the fuses were mostly of the impact-delay type usually associated with deck-piercing ammunition. This ammunition was quite useless for anti-personnel or counter-battery work. Also, most of the guns were emplaced in open concrete pits and so were easy victims of plunging fire and strafing. The few AA guns at the defence's disposal were obsolete.

So Corregidor and the Manila Bay forts fell, like Singapore, to Japanese armies which were inferior in numbers but superior in artillery. These victories, however, signalled the end of the great days of the Japanese artillery. Never again would the Imperial Japanese Army bring together masses of guns as at Singapore or Manila Bay. The early successes of the IJA in fact contributed to its demise, leading in terms of its artillery to a too-thin dispersal of contingents in 'penny-packet' garrisons throughout the Pacific and East Asia, which were subsequently dealt with piecemeal by the Allies.

Artillery also played a little-known but vital role in supporting amphibious assaults during the Allied island-hopping campaigns in the Pacific. Whenever geography allowed, as at Okinawa, small islands off the coast of the primary objective were seized and converted into fire bases for heavy guns like the 155-mm Long Toms. Tiny airstrips were built, from which observers in spotter planes could range over the objective reporting targets and directing their guns.

Whenever such arrangements could be made, the task of the assault force was made much easier. Naval bombardment was comforting but was never an adequate substitute for the support fire of land-based guns. This is because naval guns are high-velocity, flat-trajectory weapons, incapable of hitting targets behind hills and in defiles. Land-based guns, on the other hand, can hit 'hidden' targets by means of their searching type of fire.

In amphibious operations the assault force is usually at its most vulnerable while the landings are actually being

OPPOSITE *A battery of British 25-pounders mounted on a 'Z' craft in Burma. These barge mountings gave valuable mobility in jungle areas.*
ABOVE *A Japanese 37-mm Type II (1922) infantry pack howitzer with tripod.*
RIGHT *A Japanese M-90 75-mm self-propelled gun; these vehicles used the chassis of the M-97 medium tank.*

made. Support fire from naval vessels is usually lifted during this period, and the landing group is without artillery. But this was not the case whenever land-based guns were firing from positions on islets off the coast of the objective. In a variation on the same theme, British artillery firing across the Strait of Messina from Sicily very effectively covered landings at Calabria on the Italian mainland.

In the jungle the Japanese, usually plagued by inferior artillery, would go to extremes to disguise the positions of their guns and so preserve them from the powerful artillery of the Allies. For example, in operations in Northern Luzon (9 January–30 June 1945), US troops took fire from a 30-cm naval howitzer emplaced in a timber pit and covered by a native hut mounted on rails which was slid aside when the gun was to be fired. To complete the deception, all signs of military activity were removed, and the ground about the hut was planted as a garden. Other gun positions were in caves and tunnels. Such guns were never fired when US air spotters were in the vicinity and, as may be imagined, they were extremely difficult to detect.

Allied artillery played important offensive and defensive roles in the Asian operations. It was especially useful against pill-boxes, bunkers and tunnel positions. Destroying a bunker was like destroying an enormously strong, but immobile, tank. Once the bunker had been located, its cover of brush, undergrowth and other 'soft' material had to be peeled away. Howitzer fire or a thermite grenade usually sufficed for this operation. Then the bunker could be penetrated or destroyed by a sniper gun. Only high-velocity AA or AT guns could be employed for this purpose –the bigger the better. Two of the guns commonly used to snipe at bunkers were the British 2-pounder AT gun and the US 90-mm AA gun. Once the bunker had been penetrated by an AP shell, it was ready to be finished off by flame-throwers.

In general, any gun that could be dismantled for pack transport or towed along a bulldozed track had its uses in the jungle. Once the gunners had learned to co-operate closely with the infantry, artillery fire could be as devastating in the jungle as it was in other environments.

Chapter Six

The Post-War Years

During World War II several new weapons had appeared, and some older weapons had been revived in more sophisticated forms. Surface-to-surface rockets had been used extensively as artillery, especially by the Soviet and German armies, and after the war rockets and guided missiles were further improved and became a major component of the artillery arsenals of the Great Powers.

The use of nuclear weapons was certainly one of the most important developments of World War II. It was only a matter of time before the scientists would so 'package' the nuclear device that it could be delivered by relatively small-calibre weapons. The first atomic cannon was 'Atomic Annie', the US Army's 280-mm gun, which fired a nuclear shell on 25 May 1953 in a demonstration at Frenchman's Flat, Nevada. Within a few years nuclear shells were developed for the 8-inch howitzer and the 155-mm howitzer, and the Russians, too, began to exhibit heavy guns thought capable of nuclear fire. Because of the danger of escalation, no nuclear shells have been fired in combat; but the nuclear capability has nevertheless dramatically increased the destructive potential of artillery.

Other developments, many of which were initiated in World War II, have further improved the capabilities of artillery during the post-war years. SP artillery has been

improved and many more guns wedded to purpose-built SP mounts; guns have become more powerful and, through the use of new metals, especially aluminium alloys, lighter; anti-tank artillery has been improved, and so has anti-aircraft artillery – though the latter has been largely superseded by guided missiles with sophisticated homing devices; finally, in Vietnam, a new SP mount appeared – the helicopter.

ABOVE *A US 175-mm SP gun firing near Long Binh, Vietnam.* BELOW *Artillery's nuclear dawn – marked by the test firing of a nuclear shell from 'Atomic Annie', the US Army's 280-mm gun. The demonstration took place on 25 May 1953 at Frenchman's Flat, Nevada.*

The Korean War

The role of artillery in the Korean War has been consistently underestimated by military analysts. Somehow, the comparatively mundane contribution of the artillerist has been lost amid more glamorous tales of subsonic dogfights between jet interceptors in 'MiG Alley' or bitter infantry combat on far-away ridges with curious names like 'T-Bone Hill'. Inevitably, the emphasis placed upon air power by Western observers contributed to the dismal 'Press' which the artillery received after the war. In Korea, as in the Indo-China and Vietnam conflicts, air power played a less than decisive role—certainly not fulfilling the expectations of its numerous advocates. There is no more eloquent testimony to the false sense of security induced by unlimited air power than General MacArthur's prediction that any Chinese Communist intervention in Korea could be smashed with the 'greatest slaughter' by UN air power. In the event, the Red Chinese soldiers marched by night and disguised their positions by day, and not one soldier was detected until actual contact was made with the UN ground forces. At that point, of course, the task of dealing with the Red 'volunteers' became the job of the infantry and artillery (with a tip of the hat to tactical air support).

The numerically superior Communist forces were not nearly as predictable as many accounts would have us believe. The stereotyped picture of 'human wave' assaults seems inextricably linked in the Western mind with Oriental armies. But in Korea there was a vast discrepancy between the reality of disciplined troops using sophisticated infiltration tactics and the literary convention of hordes of Chinese advancing upon a ridge position, beating tin cans and blowing bugles with no support heavier than loudspeakers blaring propaganda.

At first glance the Communist armies did indeed seem primitive by Western standards, but on that score appearances were often deceiving. A further important factor was that the UN forces were numerically inferior and had only about half the number of guns fielded by the Chinese Communist Forces (CCF) and North Koreans. In such circumstances it is still more to the credit of the UN gunners that they managed to impose their will on the field of battle; their achievement included firing on aggregate 6–10 rounds to every round fired by their enemies.

The Chinese Communist Army, founded in 1927 as the Workers' and Peasants' Red Army, had been forged into a formidable fighting force through a history of almost constant conflict. By 1950 Soviet equipment of World War

OPPOSITE *A captured 85-mm AA gun of Russian origin seen near Pyongyang, Korea.*
LEFT *A North Korean (ex-Russian) SU-76 SP gun captured during the drive towards the Naktong River, September 1950.*
BELOW *British gunners prepare their 25-pounder for firing on the Han River Front in March 1951.*

II vintage, with a slight admixture of captured Japanese guns, constituted the bulk of the artillery. Soviet tactical doctrine dominated the thinking of the CCF's artillerists.

This emphasis on Soviet doctrine and equipment meant, among other things, that the CCF had a large number of light mortars for close infantry support, with 76-mm field guns used in masses at the divisional level. A small quantity of 122-mm and 152-mm howitzers and guns was also spread about to add weight to the Red barrages. The M-13

Katyusha rocket batteries were still in use, though the Soviets gradually replaced these with the improved 140-mm 13M-14 rocket batteries. Much the same situation prevailed in the artillery arm of the North Korean Army.

The relatively low rate of fire of the Red gunners, mentioned above, was more the product of poor logistics than lack of training. Nevertheless, their mortars caused a great number of casualties. Some 35% of UN troops killed and 75% of those wounded were victims of artillery fire.

ABOVE *A battery of US anti-aircraft guns near Pusan, Korea.*
BELOW *US marines look on as an artillery team fires its 8-inch howitzer, seen here in full recoil.*

OPPOSITE *American 155-mm 'Long Toms' of World War II vintage release a barrage against a Communist position a few miles north of Seoul, May 1951.*

Moreover, the CCF and North Korean AA artillery, equipped chiefly with light 37-mm and Soviet medium 85-mm AA guns, accounted for 87% of all UN aircraft lost. This record is all the more remarkable considering the absence of anything approaching modern fire-control systems in the Red armies.

The artillery used by UN forces in Korea consisted almost wholly of US and British guns of World War II vintage. The hardest-used guns were the US 105-mm and 155-mm howitzers; a total of 900,000 tons of 105-mm and 155-mm howitzer ammunition was expended in the course of the war. This was almost as much ammunition as had been fired in the Mediterranean and Pacific theatres during World War II.

The protective barrage of World War I was revived in the form of intense 'flash fires', which could be called in to cover the front of any beleaguered position with an impassable screen of HE. Fire-direction techniques had become so advanced, and the response to calls for fire missions so instantaneous, that enemy movement within the range of UN guns was severely hampered. The best example of this was the famous 'Wonjou Shoot' of February 1951. In this action UN air reconnaisance spotted two or three North Korean infantry divisions in the open and called for artillery fire on the target. After some three hours of intensive fire 3,500 North Koreans lay dead near Wonjou, their divisions comprehensively destroyed.

A persistent problem for UN gunners in Korea was deciding where to place the guns. Much of Korea is either hill, mountain or paddy, little of which is suitable for the deployment of artillery. This made the need for SP mounts acute (and in due course significantly more SP guns were designed and built as a result of the Korean experience). Also, Communist infiltration tactics forced artillerists on many occasions to defend their guns in hand-to-hand combat. Such actions usually involved firing HE and WP (white phosphorous) shells into enemy infantry at very short range and eventually led to the revival of case shot as an artillery round.

Because of the special terrain problems in Korea, the most indispensable artillery pieces were mortars and recoilless rifles. These were infantry weapons, easily transported over rough terrain and quite effective in the close-support role. Two SP types of AA battery were found invaluable in this role: one was the Quad-50, mounting four ·50-calibre Browning heavy machine guns; the other was the M-19 motor carriage, mounting two 40-mm Bofors guns.

Ordeal of Dien Bien Phu

The biggest and most decisive battle of the Indo-China War (1946–54) was the 55-day siege of the French fortress at Dien Bien Phu. The French had purposely placed a small army of paratroopers and men of the Foreign Legion in the valley round the village of Dien Bien Phu in the hope that they could lure a large force of Ho Chi Minh's Vietminh rebels into a set-piece battle and there annihilate them.

The position of the French Union force was highly vulnerable. They occupied a valley surrounded by precipitous hills covered with thick jungle growth. Normally an army in such a position, entirely surrounded by enemy forces, would consider its situation perilous. But the French had the utmost contempt for the Vietminh. They knew that the rebel army had 105-mm howitzers and 75-mm pack howitzers, captured from American forces in Korea. However, they not only thought the Vietminh gunners incompetent, they also decided that they would not be able to transport their guns through the mountains to within range of Dien Bien Phu. As the French saw the coming battle, the Vietminh would be decimated as they attacked the forts by a deadly combination of artillery fire and napalm bombs.

But, though the French were baiting the trap, it was to be the Vietminh who would spring it. Chinese instructors had trained the gunners of General Vu Hien's 351st Heavy Division to a high degree of proficiency. Furthermore, by the most extraordinary labour, all the guns of this division had been dismantled and transported through hundreds of miles of forbidding jungle terrain to Dien Bien Phu.

Throughout January and February 1954, the Vietminh carefully emplaced their guns and mortars. In March they began to bombard the French positions in earnest.

Much depended upon the control of Dien Bien Phu's airstrip. If the Communist artillery came close enough to dispute its use, the fortress's only link with the outside would be severed. The French artillery commander, Colonel Piroth, had vowed to destroy any Vietminh gun careless enough to reveal its position by firing. He had also refused adequately to fortify the position of his 155-mm howitzers, dismissing the suggestion with the pithy answer: 'Who could hit them?' But the Vietminh were not rank amateurs in the matter of camouflage and concealment, and they soon rendered the airstrip useless by their fire. Piroth was unable to locate many of the Vietminh guns. He committed suicide with a grenade on 14 March. By then the

French were having to resort to air drops to supply the fortress.

Soon even the air drops became dangerous and haphazard. The Vietminh were employing about 20 Russian Bofors-type 37-mm AA guns to create a 'flak envelope' around the French positions in the valley. Consequently, the transport planes involved in the air drops were forced to release their cargoes from altitudes of over 8,000 feet in order to avoid the fire of the Vietminh guns.

French attempts to interdict the supply trails of the Vietminh by aerial bombardment were met by flak concentrations comparable to that encountered during World War II by Allied bombers over the Ruhr.

On 7 May Dien Bien Phu was taken by storm. In the course of the siege the Vietminh artillery had fired 100,000 shells. The French, in planning the operation, had overlooked the possibility of the Vietminh seriously challenging their air and artillery supremacy. This was a grievous error. In the end the Vietminh gunners broke the back of the defence, turned the supply effort into a shambles and prevented the French from disrupting their own supply lines. Their efforts thus made a significant contribution to one of the decisive battles of our era.

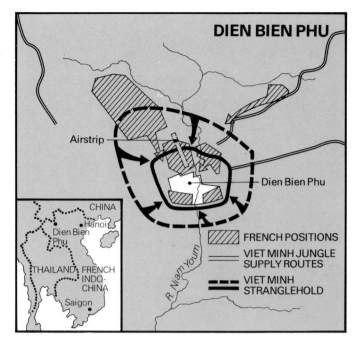

OPPOSITE *French troops occupy the doomed garrison.*
BELOW LEFT *An early parachute drop falls inside the perimeter.*
BOTTOM LEFT *Jungle fires burn beside the vulnerable airstrip.*
BELOW *Tending the wounded; their commander has committed suicide.*

Tube Artillery since World War II

Conventional artillery has undoubtedly forfeited some of its functions to rockets and missiles, but it is clear from recent experience that missile weapons have by no means superseded guns. In fact, conventional artillery seems to have experienced something of a resurgence in recent years, while missiles have become less faddish. This trend is strongly indicated in several ways. One has been the continuing emphasis on conventional guns in the armed forces of the Soviet Union. It is now estimated that one-third of the Soviet ground army consists of artillery, and most of the weapons of this arm are conventional tube artillery.

capable of penetrating the armour of the newer Soviet tanks. Had the Soviets made a thrust into central Europe at that time, there would have been no way of stopping them short of using nuclear weapons–a move which would undoubtedly have plunged the world into the nightmare of total war. As a consequence of this scare, the USA modernized its conventional ground forces; in 1962 the ROAD Division, an infantry division with significantly more conventional firepower, was created as the basic operational unit of the US Army.

The Korean War was fought mainly with conventional artillery of World War II vintage, which was not suited to the requirements of modern warfare. Soon after the Korean War the NATO nations began to produce radically advanced SP support guns. Most of these new weapons

Another pointer was provided by the vast programme for modernizing its conventional weapons that was carried out by the US Army during the Kennedy administration. A major target of this programme, which cost $1,800,000,000, was the artillery.

This revival of conventional artillery must not be seen as indicative of a retreat from technology. It is, rather, an admission that, if we are all to survive, some way must be found to meet a variety of threats to world peace. The Communist Bloc, for example, has maintained large conventionally equipped ground forces at peak efficiency throughout the post-war decades. In 1961, at the height of the Berlin crisis, it was discovered that the AP (armour-piercing) ammunition issued to American units was not

have fully enclosed fighting compartments with all-round traverse. Some of them incorporate defence systems against ABC (atomic, bacteriological and chemical) weapons. Such systems will allow the crew to operate the gun in relative safety on the 'deserted battlefields' of the future. NATO SP guns, with the exception of the German Jagdpanzer 90-mm tank-hunter, follow the traditional emphasis of the Western Allies on the support, rather than the assault, role.

The Soviets have never really strayed very far from conventional artillery, even in more recent times. In fact, the development and production of new conventional guns to replace the USSR's elderly World War II armoury was proceeding as that war ended, and was to continue for at least a decade. The first objectives of the renewal programme

OPPOSITE AND LEFT *Vietnam—the men and the guns of Fire Base Carroll bombard the unseen foe.*

ABOVE *A US marine at Conthien fires his 81-mm mortar on a North Vietnamese position.*

were the anti-tank and anti-aircraft guns. Two very powerful anti-tank guns had been developed too late to see much action in the war. These were the M-1944 100-mm field gun, which was used as a heavy AT gun at corps level, and the D-44 85-mm divisional gun. The D-44 remained the standard divisional piece until 1955, but the M-1945 85-mm AT gun soon replaced it as the divisional AT gun. The M-1945 85-mm AT gun was a very advanced design with an auxiliary engine and a trail-mounted castor wheel which allowed it to move under its own power when unlimbered. The new AA guns were the M-1949 100-mm AA gun, which replaced the 85-mm AA gun of World War II, and the M-1955 122-mm AA gun. With these guns, the Soviets began to use off-carriage radar and directors, thus serving notice on the other Powers that their technology was much improved. Indeed, there is evidence that the Soviet-built 37-mm light flak guns used by the Vietminh at Dien Bien Phu incorporated radar range-finders.

In 1955 the Soviets further renewed their artillery with advanced models of several familiar calibres. The M-1955 203-mm gun-howitzer was the first modern Soviet heavy

gun since 1940. It replaced several obsolescent pieces, including the M-1935 152-mm gun, the M-1931 203-mm howitzer and the M-1939 280-mm howitzer. The new gun was similar to the US 8-inch howitzer and was thought to have an atomic-shell capability.

In the design of their new guns, the Soviets have incorporated all the virtues of their wartime family of guns—mobility, firepower, simplicity and standardization. The artillery doctrine of World War II seems also to have been retained to a large extent, and artillery is still regarded as the main strike force. Anti-tank and assault guns remain the most prominent battlefield types, although lately the USSR has been building more SP support guns.

This new emphasis on SP support guns may indicate that the Soviets are trying to close the gap between their artillery and that of the Western Powers. Soviet heavy artillery—unlike the other types we have looked at—has never been very mobile or very flexible. This was of very little consequence in World War II because, from 1943 anyway, the Soviet Air Force controlled the air space above the guns and prevented destructive strikes by the Luftwaffe.

The Arab-Israeli War of 1967 revealed, however, the flaw in Soviet doctrine. The Army of the UAR was equipped with Soviet tanks and guns and followed Soviet tactical doctrine. The Israeli Army was equipped with American, British and French tanks and guns. Most Israeli guns were SP support guns, including some heavy types on Israeli-designed mounts. These guns acted in support of Israeli armour but did not operate directly behind the tanks. The technique used was one developed by the British during the fighting in the Western Desert in World War II. The SPs followed the tanks but stayed beyond the range of the enemy's tank and anti-tank guns. Thus, they could operate in relative safety and, by using indirect fire, provide artillery support for the armour. With this method, too, the limited traverse of SP artillery may be utilized to best advantage. Arab heavy artillery, on the other hand, was towed to a fixed position and, more often than not, remained there after Israeli armour had bypassed it or the Israeli Air Force had bombed and strafed the position. It was soon evident that Soviet-built heavy guns simply could not function effectively on a modern battlefield.

OPPOSITE *North Vietnamese coastal batteries point seaward manned by soldiers of the People's Army.*
ABOVE *Anti-aircraft defences near the Ham Zhong Bridge in North Vietnam during an American air-raid.*

Rocket Artillery

Rocket artillery became very fashionable after World War II. Strong precedents had been set by Germany's success with the Nebelwerfer series of area-fire weapons and Maultier SP rocket launchers; by Russia's use of powerful batteries of Katyusha multiple-tube launchers, and by the devastating effect of Allied rocket bombardments in amphibious operations. The development of area-fire batteries continued after the war, and a relatively new type of rocket weapon, the guided missile, was intensively

TITAN II LAUNCH

ABOVE *A V-1 flying bomb, ancestor of today's rocket artillery, photographed immediately after being launched.*
LEFT *The Titan II, a US two-stage Inter Continental Ballistic Missile (ICBM), maximum range 6,300 miles, rears from its launch pad at the USAF Missile Test Center at Cape Kennedy.*
OPPOSITE *A US tactical rocket, Honest John (range 24 miles), is fired during manoeuvres in West Germany in 1955.*

developed for a variety of field and long-range bombardment roles. The main types produced for land warfare are as follows:

Surface-to-surface. This is a comprehensive category which includes rocket weapons as diverse as mammoth ICBMs (intercontinental ballistic missiles) and the Davy Crockett, a diminutive rocket which can deliver a low-yield atomic shell over a distance of two miles yet may be launched from a tripod or light vehicle.

Free rockets (unguided) fired from multiple-tube rocket launchers continued to be the most prevalent form of rocket artillery in the Soviet Army during the post-war years. The M-13 Katyusha was replaced by a variety of similar weapons from the M13-14 140-mm rocket launcher to the M-31 300-mm launcher. These area-fire weapons were considered adequate for Soviet needs at the time but they had certain inherent limitations which would probably preclude their appearance on any modern battlefield – although the Katyusha was used by Communist forces in

Korea and Indo-China. They were simple, mobile batteries with very little recoil, but they gave off a prominent back-blast when fired and had to be used in masses, since the rockets were inaccurate and erratic in flight.

By 1960 the Soviets had developed the FROG (free rocket over-ground) series which corresponded roughly to the first generation of US tactical rockets. In this area the Soviets (still limited by primitive technology) were far behind the Americans, who had developed operational tactical missiles, both guided and free, by the early 1950s.

US guided missile research in World War II was extensive. Two simple operational missiles, the Bat air-to-ship missile and the Azon air-to-ground guided bomb, were developed and used successfully in combat. These missiles were the ancestors of the 'smart bombs' used in Vietnam. Their guidance systems and control apparatuses have subsequently been refined, and these and other projects formed the basis for continuing programmes of post-war research.

The US Army's first combat-ready guided missile for ground support was the Corporal (1953). The Corporal

was soon followed by a series of tactical and strategic rockets. The Davy Crockett, mentioned above, was a close-support rocket with a range of two miles, comparable to that of the 81-mm and 4·2-inch mortars. Little John (range 12½ miles) and Honest John (range 24 miles) were conceived as tactical rockets roughly comparable in range to the divisional and heavy artillery then in service. The first US long-range (strategic) missile was the experimental Redstone, which was a copy of the German V-2 of World War II (as was the Soviet T-1). The operational strategic missiles included the Serjeant (range 75+ miles) and the Pershing (range 400+ miles).

Any one of these rockets can deliver a heavier and more destructive conventional projectile than comparable tube artillery weapons, while there is of course no gun with a range even close to that attained by the Pershing's warhead. But these missiles are something less than accurate; nevertheless, nuclear shells fired from conventional artillery, though lighter, are sufficiently powerful more than to offset the disparity in weight of the projectiles.

Anti-tank rockets. A great variety of anti-tank rockets has been developed in recent years. Simple infantry projectors, like the Panzerfaust and its derivatives, or the bazooka, are not strictly speaking artillery, but both they and the larger AT missiles utilize a HEAT shaped-charge projectile to 'kill' a tank (HEAT=high explosive anti-tank). These projectiles are best delivered by smooth-bore guns or rockets, since the spin imparted by a gun's rifling tends to dissipate the effect of the jet by dispersing it upon impact.

Anti-tank rockets are quite deadly–one hit usually puts a tank out of action–but they suffer from the usual rocket-weapon handicaps, including low velocity and low acceleration, both of which allow the target time to manoeuvre and so reduce the chances of scoring a hit.

Most AT missiles are wire-guided, that is, controlled by the gunner after firing by means of electronic impulses sent along fine wires played out by the rocket in flight. In effect, the gunner 'steers' the rocket onto the target. This is by no means a foolproof system, and there are ongoing experiments with infra-red, laser and computer

guidance systems. The best recent developments are the 152-mm Shillelagh 'sure-kill' missile, which follows an infra-red beam to its target, and the TOW (a tube-launched, optically tracked, wire-guided AT missile). The TOW missile will hit its target so long as the gunner keeps the launching tube's telescopic sight focused on it.

Anti-aircraft rockets. The British made some limited use of AA rockets during World War II, and the Germans were in production with their Luftfaust, a multiple-tube hand-held rocket-launcher, at the war's end. These early AA missiles were in fact relatively unsophisticated barrage-fire weapons.

Modern AA missiles utilize various types of guidance systems. Nearly all have electronic 'brains' and 'eyes' which perform a variety of functions. The earliest sophisticated AA missiles, like the Nike (operational in 1954), were 'beam riders' which followed a radar beam to their targets. Nike, and its successors, Nike Ajax and Nike-B, intercept at twice the speed of sound and have a slant range of 18–23 miles.

These missiles were designed to intercept high-flying strategic bombers and have been installed in permanent emplacements near US cities and industrial areas. But today ICBMs and IRBMs (intermediate-range ballistic missiles) constitute the most important long-range bombardment threat. Nike cannot intercept these missiles. Surface-to-air missile research today concentrates on developing an ABM (anti-ballistic missile) which could intercept an ICBM.

Nike has proved adequate for defence against strategic bombers, but other SAMs are needed to intercept tactical aircraft. Most missiles used against low-flying aircraft have homing devices which react to signals sent out by the target aircraft. The sensor device is usually a radar set or a photo-electric eye sensitive to heat. Some of the US missiles in this category are Hawk and Chaparral. In the Arab-Israeli War of 1973, the Egyptians took a heavy initial toll of Israeli aircraft with their Russian-built SAMs, mostly of the SAM-6 variety; these seriously inhibited the Israelis' tactical strike effort until the missile sites were overrun.

OPPOSITE *The TOW anti-tank system, by which a wire-guided AT missile with a range limit of 2,200 yards is launched from a firing tube and optically tracked along its path to the target. The TOW system can be mounted on a variety of vehicles, including helicopters.*

TOP *A US Hawk surface-to-air missile (SAM), used primarily against low-flying tactical aircraft.*

ABOVE *The Davy Crockett, a close-support ground rocket with a range of two miles.*

RIGHT *The US Nike Ajax on its launcher; this anti-aircraft rocket, now superseded by the Nike Hercules, was designed to intercept high-flying strategic bombers.*

From this brief account it will be evident that rocket development has already reached a point at which there are rockets capable of fulfilling all the functions of conventional tube artillery. This has led some to predict that missile artillery will eventually replace conventional forms. The school of experience, however, has taught the necessity of maintaining a balance in the field, and the predicted obsolescence of cannon has so far not come to pass.

DATA SECTION
I: Details of Important Weapons

World War I period

French 75-mm field gun M-1897

The first modern Quick–Firing field gun. In service by 1898, it became the standard field gun of both the French Army and the American Expeditionary Force.

Calibre	75 mm
Range	7,500 yards
Elevation	— 10 to + 19 degrees
Traverse	6 degrees
Weight	2,513 pounds
Muzzle velocity	2,047 feet per second
Rate of fire	12 rounds per minute

Austrian Skoda 30·5-cm field mortar M-1911

Nicknamed 'Schlanke (slim) Emma'; used in the attack on the Liège forts in 1914. A very mobile heavy field mortar.

Calibre	305 mm
Range	10,500 yards
Elevation	+ 45 to + 75 degrees
Weight	24 tons
Rate of fire	1 round per 6 minutes
Weight of shell	838 pounds

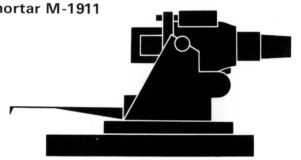

German 77-mm field gun C96 n/A

Standard German field gun in World War I until replaced by the FK-16 beginning in 1916; remained especially effective in the anti–tank role.

Calibre	77 mm
Range	9,186 yards
Elevation	— 12 to + 16 degrees
Traverse	8 degrees
Weight	1,930 pounds
Muzzle velocity	1,525 fps

German 77-mm field gun FK-16

Improved 77-mm field gun; replaced the C 96 n/A from 1916 onwards.

Calibre	77 mm
Range	11,264 yards
Elevation	— 9·5 to + 35 degrees
Traverse	4 degrees
Weight	2,750 pounds
Muzzle velocity	1,968 fps

German 105-mm light field howitzer 98/09

The 105-mm was the standard German field howitzer in World War I.

Calibre	105 mm
Range	7,655 yards
Elevation	− 13 to + 40 degrees
Traverse	4 degrees
Weight	2,250 pounds
Muzzle velocity	991 fps

British 6-inch howitzer

The standard British medium howitzer in World War I. Used also in early World War II campaigns.

Calibre	152·4 mm
Range	11,400 yards
Elevation	0 to + 45 degrees
Traverse	8 degrees
Weight	9,318 pounds
	(travelling position)
Muzzle velocity	1,352 fps
Rate of fire	2 rpm

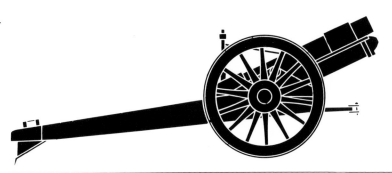

World War II and after

Soviet 122-mm howitzer M-1938

This gun used the same carriage as the 152-mm (D-1) M-1943 howitzer. It could be fired without spreading the trails but had a traverse of only 1·5 degrees if fired in this manner.

Calibre	122 mm
Range	13,000 yards
Elevation	− 3 to + 63·5 degrees
Traverse	49 degrees
Weight	5,510 pounds
	(travelling position)
Muzzle velocity	1,700 fps
Rate of fire	5–6 rpm
Penetration	7·87 inches at 0 degrees

Swedish Bofors 40-mm AA gun

This Bofors 1936 model was adopted by the USA, Britain and Russia as their standard medium AA gun. Some were also used by the Japanese and Germans in World War II.

Calibre	40 mm
Range	23,200 feet (vertical)
	16,200 feet (effective ceiling)
	12,300 yards (horizontal)
Elevation	− 5 to + 90 degrees
Traverse	360 degrees
Weight	4,234 pounds
Muzzle velocity	2,950 fps
Rate of fire	80– 120 rpm

German 50-mm AT gun Pak 38

Standard German anti-tank gun in North
Africa; subsequently replaced by 75-mm
Pak 40.

Calibre	50 mm
Range	3,000 yards
Elevation	—13 to +22·5 degrees
Traverse	60 degrees
Weight	2,016 pounds
Muzzle velocity	2,953–3,280 fps
Rate of fire	16 rpm
Penetration	71 mm at 30 degrees at 600 yards

German 75-mm AT gun Pak 40

A product of the gun-armour race, this
anti-tank gun took over from the 50-mm
Pak 38 beginning in late 1942 and remained in
service for the rest of the war.

Calibre	75 mm
Range	8,750 yards
Elevation	—5 to +22 degrees
Traverse	60 degrees
Weight	3,350 pounds
Muzzle velocity	3,070 fps
Rate of fire	12–15 rpm
Penetration	3·43 inches at 30 degrees at 1,000 yards

US 75-mm M-1 A-1 pack howitzer

A low-velocity howitzer well-suited to both
mule and air transport.

Calibre	75 mm
Range	9,600 yards
Elevation	—5 to +45 degrees
Traverse	6 degrees
Weight	1,442 pounds
Muzzle velocity	1,250 fps
Rate of fire	6 rpm

US 90-mm M-2 mobile AA gun

The standard US AA gun in World War II,
developed also for AT use.

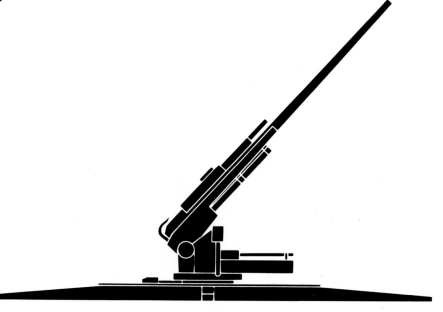

Calibre	90 mm
Range	33,800 feet (vertical) 18,890 yards (horizontal)
Elevation	—10 to +80 degrees
Traverse	360 degrees
Weight	14·0 tons
Muzzle velocity	2,700 fps
Rate of fire	20–30 rpm
Time to emplace	7 minutes

US 37-mm AT gun M-3 A-1

This gun closely resembles and was modelled on the German Rheinmetall 37-mm Pak 35/36.

Calibre	37 mm
Range	13,000 yards
Elevation	— 10 to + 15 degrees
Traverse	60 degrees
Weight	912 pounds
Muzzle velocity	2,640 fps
Rate of fire	25 rpm
Penetration	2·4 inches at 20 degrees at 520 yards

Soviet 57-mm AT gun M-1943

This gun was based on the successful 57-mm AT gun M-1941 but utilized a modern tubular split trail instead of a box section trail. It used the same carriage as the 76-mm gun M-1942.

Calibre	57 mm
Range	9,200 yards
Elevation	— 5 to + 25 degrees
Traverse	56 degrees
Weight	2,535 pounds
Muzzle velocity	4,200 fps
Rate of fire	20—25 rpm
Penetration	5·5 inches at 0 degrees at 550 yards

British 25-pounder gun-howitzer Mark 2

By the beginning of the Western Desert campaign this gun had replaced the 18-pounder field gun and the 4·5-inch howitzer as the standard British field artillery weapon.

Calibre	87·6 mm
Range	13,400 yards
Elevation	— 5 to + 40 degrees
Traverse	8 degrees (without travelling field platform)
Weight	7,335 pounds
Muzzle velocity	1,485 fps
Rate of fire	5 rpm
Penetration	2·52 inches at 30 degrees at 1,000 yards

Soviet Katyusha 132-mm rocket launcher M-13

The battery was fired electrically from the cab of the truck. Two jacks at the rear of the truck's chassis added stability during launching. The Katyusha was subsequently replaced by the 140-mm 13M-14, a similar weapon encountered by UN forces in Korea.

Rails	8
Rockets	16
Weight	6·4 tons (launcher and truck)
Elevation	+ 15 to + 45 degrees
Velocity	1,150 fps
Range	9,900 yards
Time to reload	6–10 minutes

British 2-pounder AT gun

Standard British AT gun in the Western
Desert until replaced by the 6-pounder
Mark 2.

Calibre	40 mm
Range	500 yards (effective)
Elevation	−13 to +15 degrees
Traverse	360 degrees
Weight	1,848 pounds
	(travelling position)
Muzzle velocity	2,616 fps
Rate of fire	22 rpm

Soviet 76-mm field gun M-1942 (Chinese Communist Type 54)

This gun was similar to the 76-mm field gun
M-1939 in most respects but was fitted with a
muzzle brake and was mounted on a modified
57-mm AT gun carriage with split tubular
trails. Its light weight contributed to a
certain instability in action (note high muzzle
velocity).

Calibre	76 mm
Range	14,600 yards
Elevation	−5 to +37 degrees
Traverse	54 degrees
Weight	2,460 pounds
	(travelling position)
Muzzle velocity	3,100 fps
Rate of fire	15 rpm
Penetration	3·62 inches at 0 degrees at
	550 yards

Soviet 76-mm support gun SU-76

This assault gun was constructed on the
chassis of the T-70 light tank. Its open
superstructure made the crew vulnerable.

Weight	12·3 tons
Length	16 feet 5 inches (without
	gun tube overhang)
Width	8 feet 10 inches
Height	7 feet 2 inches
Speed	28 mph
Range	224 miles
Armament	76 mm gun with 60 rounds
Elevation	−5 to +25 degrees
Traverse	30 degrees
Armour	0·98 inches (max.)
Crew	4

Soviet 100-mm assault gun SU-100

The SU-100 was constructed on the T-34
medium tank chassis.

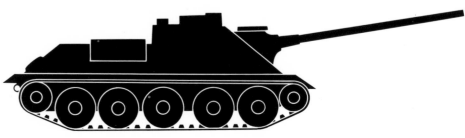

Weight	33·1 tons
Length	19 feet 8 inches (without
	gun tube overhang)
Width	9 feet 9 inches
Height	7 feet 6 inches
Speed	35 mph
Range	190 miles
Armament	100 mm gun with 34 rounds
Elevation	−2 to +17 degrees
Traverse	32 degrees
Crew	4

Soviet 122-mm assault gun JSU-122A

This gun was constructed on the JS heavy tank chassis.

Weight	51·2 tons
Length	22 feet 4 inches (without gun tube overhang)
Width	10 feet 0 inches
Height	8 feet 1 inch
Speed	23 mph
Range	85 miles
Armament	122 mm D-25 gun redesignated D-25S, with 30 rounds
Elevation	—3 to +20 degrees
Traverse	20 degrees
Crew	4

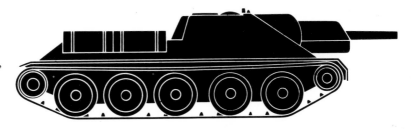

Soviet 152-mm heavy assault gun JSU-152

The JSU-152 was an imposing weapon but was limited by its great weight and the small amount of ammunition carried. In terms of specifications this behemoth was a near-duplicate of the JSU-122A, with the following exceptions:

Armament	152 mm gun with 20 rounds
Crew	5

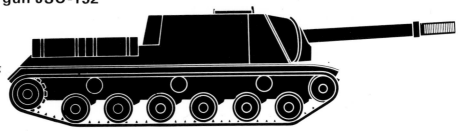

British 17-pounder AT gun Mark I

This gun is easily recognized by its low silhouette (5 feet 6 inches), prominent double-baffle muzzle brake and spaced armour shield with scalloped edge on top.

Calibre	76·2 mm
Range	11,500 yards
Elevation	—6 to +16·5 degrees
Traverse	60 degrees
Weight	6,700 pounds (travelling position)
Muzzle velocity	3,100 fps
Rate of fire	20 rpm
Penetration	9·13 inches at 1,100 yards

Japanese 70-mm howitzer Type 92

This small infantry support weapon was ideal for fighting in jungle areas or difficult terrain. It was easily manhandled or broken down for transport into three pack loads. An identical weapon was manufactured by the Chinese Communist Army.

Calibre	70 mm
Range	3,000 yards
Elevation	—11 to +70 degrees
Traverse	45 degrees
Weight	468 pounds
Muzzle velocity	650 fps
Rate of fire	4–6 rpm

British 5·5-inch gun Mark 3

Issued in 1941 as a replacement for the
obsolescent 6-inch howitzer. Equivalent to the
German heavy divisional gun. A prominent
recognition feature of the Mark 3 were the
large vertical equilibrators.

Calibre	140 mm
Range	17,000 yards
Elevation	— 5 to + 45 degrees
Traverse	60 degrees
Weight	12,850 pounds
	(travelling position)
Muzzle velocity	1,675 fps
Rate of fire	2 rpm

US 155-mm M-1 mount M-4 gun M-1918

This was a self-propelled gun created by
wedding the World War I vintage 155-mm
GPF gun and the M-3 medium tank chassis.
It was also the first American SP gun to
incorporate the large rear-end recoil spade as a
design feature.

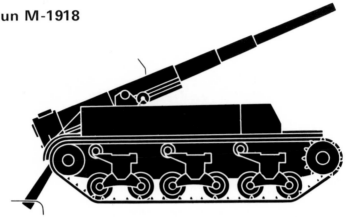

Calibre	155 mm
Range	18,700 yards
Elevation	— 5 to + 30 degrees
Traverse	28 degrees
Weight	25·9 tons
Muzzle velocity	2,410 fps
Rate of fire	4 rpm

US M-2 A-1 mount M-4 howitzer

This SP gun was commonly called the
'Priest'. The M-7 howitzer motor carriage
mounted the reliable M-2 A-1 105-mm
howitzer, and a heavy machine gun was
provided for secondary armament in a pulpit-
like open mount.

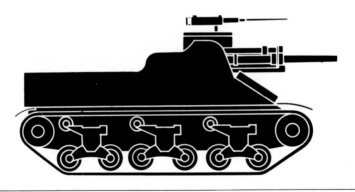

Calibre	105 mm
Range	12,200 yards
Elevation	— 5 to + 32 degrees
Traverse	L-12, R-25 degrees
Weight	23·2 tons
Muzzle velocity	1,550 fps
Rate of fire	4 rpm

German quad 20-mm AA gun (2-cm Flakvierling 38)

Standard German light Flak in World War II,
it consisted of four 20-mm Flak 38 guns on a
quadruple mount. The magazines of two
guns could be changed while the remaining
two fired. Sometimes mounted on tank
chassis or half-tracks.

Calibre	20 mm
Range	12,465 feet (vertical)
	7,215 feet
	(effective ceiling)
	5,230 yards (horizontal)
Elevation	— 10 to + 100 degrees
Traverse	360 degrees
Weight	2,979 pounds
Muzzle velocity	2,950 fps (HE)
	2,720 fps (AP)
Rate of fire	700–800 rpm

US 155-mm M-1 and M-1 A-1 gun

The famous 'Long Tom'. This gun replaced the 155-mm M-1 GPF gun M-1918 of World War I vintage as the principal long-range heavy artillery piece in the US arsenal.

Calibre	155 mm
Range	25,395 yards
Elevation	− 1 to + 63 degrees
Traverse	60 degrees
Weight	13·3 tons
Muzzle velocity	2,800 fps
Rate of fire	1 rpm
Time to emplace	30 minutes

US 8-inch M-1 howitzer

This was the workhorse of the Allied Artillery effort in World War II.

Calibre	203·2 mm
Range	18,510 yards
Elevation	− 2 to + 65 degrees
Traverse	60 degrees
Weight	12·5 tons
Muzzle velocity	1,950 pounds
Rate of fire	1 rpm
Time to emplace	30–60 minutes

US 3-inch AT gun M-5

This was the largest pure anti-tank gun built by the United States during World War II.

Calibre	81 mm
Range	16,100 yards
Elevation	− 5 to + 30 degrees
Traverse	45 degrees
Weight	4,785 pounds
Muzzle velocity	2,800 fps
Rate of fire	20 rpm

US 120-mm AA gun M-1

An excellent heavy anti-aircraft gun. Though not the largest AA gun produced during World War II, it out-performed all others.

Calibre	120 mm
Range	47,400 feet (vertical)
	27,100 yards (horizontal)
Elevation	− 5 to + 80 degrees
Traverse	360 degrees continuous
Weight	21·8 tons
Muzzle velocity	3,100 fps
Rate of fire	12 rpm
Time to emplace	40 minutes

2: Types of Shells

Gas shell: for French 75-mm field gun M-1897

This French shell was the prototype of all successful gas shells used in World War I. The bursting charge was just strong enough to crack the shell open. Too large a charge would have dispersed the gas over a wide area, rendering it ineffective. Gas was not used in World War II.

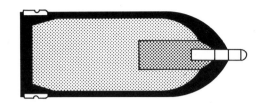

World War I Shell: Shrapnel

This is modern shrapnel, not to be confused with spherical case or early shrapnel, a type of shell invented by Lieutenant Henry Shrapnel and first used in 1804. Modern shrapnel was developed in the 1880s and was used extensively in World War I. It might best be described as an airborne canister round. Shrapnel was of little use against field works or dispersed infantry and was soon discarded.

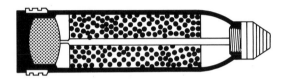

HE: High explosive

The standard projectile for use against personnel or 'soft targets'. This shell depends primarily upon blast for effect, but the shower of fine steel splinters from its casing will kill infantry in the open.

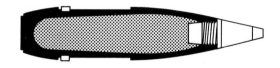

HVAP: Hyper velocity armour-piercing

This is a modern composite rigid armour-piercing shot considered to be about 50% more effective than standard AP, although about 60% lighter because of the aluminium sheath. It is really a sabot-type round in which the sheath (sabot) disintegrates when the projectile strikes the target. Only the hard tungsten carbide core penetrates. HVAP was the standard AP round for Gerlich AT guns.

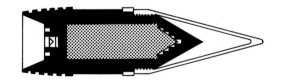

HEAT: High explosive anti-tank

This shell utilizes a physical principle to penetrate armour that was discovered by the American engineer Monroe (the Monroe effect). When the shell strikes the target the shaped charge is detonated by the base fuse and becomes a very hot flame which, because of the shape of the charge, will burst forward in a thin jet and literally sear its way through armour.

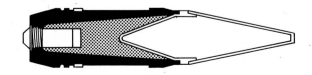

Index

Page numbers in *italics* refer to captions.

Acknowledgments

The publishers would like to thank the following individuals and organizations for their kind permission to reproduce the pictures in this book:
CAMERA PRESS LONDON: 2–3, 4–5, 124, 125 all, 126, 127 both, 128, 129; CENTRAL OFFICE OF INFORMATION PHOTOGRAPHS DIVISION: 83; HEERESGESCHICHTLES MUSEUM, VIENNA: 30–31; IMPERIAL WAR MUSEUM: 14, 16, 17, 55 centre, 75 below, 82, 88 above, 96 below, 106–7, 107 above, 130 above right; ANNE HORTON: 30 below; KEYSTONE PRESS AGENCY: 76 above, 123; LIBRARY OF CONGRESS: 1, 12–13 below, 18 above, 20 below, 21 below, 25, 26 above, 27 above, 33 all, 36–37, 40 above, 41 below, 42–3 above, 45 below, 48 above, 54 inset, 60–61, 68 all, 71 above, 76 below, 85 all, 88 below, 90 below, 93 below, 98 above, 100 below, 101 below, 107 below; NATIONAL ARCHIVES WASHINGTON, D.C.: 9, 20 above, 21 below, 24 above, 32 centre and below, 34 centre and below, 35 both, 37 above and below, 38 both, 39 below, 43 below, 44 both, 45 above, 48 centre and below, 49, 52, 53 both, 56 above right and below, 57, 61 all, 65 above, 66–7 all, 72 below, 77 below, 80, 84 centre and below, 89, 92, 93 above, 96–7, 98 below, 102, 105 below, 108, 117 both; NATIONAL ARMY MUSEUM: 12 above, 40–41, 41 above; PENNSYLVANIA ACADEMY OF FINE ARTS: 26–27 below; RADIO TIMES HULTON PICTURE LIBRARY: 29, 31 below, 32 above; ROBERT HUNT LIBRARY: 13 above, 82–3, 103 above; SIGNAL MAGAZINE: 6; SMITHSONIAN INSTITUTION: 71 below; ULLSTEIN VERLAG: 97 below; UNITED STATES AIR FORCE: 130 centre left; UNITED STATES ARMY: 24 below, 34 above, 42 below, 54, 55 below, 64, 65 below, 75 above, 81, 84 above, 90 above, 103 below, 104, 105 above, 109, 112, 116, 118–119, 120, 121 both, 122 both, 132, 133 centre left; USIA/NATIONAL ARCHIVES: 131, 133 right and above left; VALENTINE MUSEUM: 18 below, 19; JACKET ILLUSTRATIONS: (front) Camera Press; (back) Camera Press; ENDPAPERS: Library of Congress; back flap: Radio Times Hulton Picture Library.
The maps and diagrams in the text and the data section were prepared specially for this book by ARKA Cartographics Ltd. The artwork and the front flap was prepared by Peter Sarsons. Extracts on pages 81 and 97 courtesy of Methuen and Co. Ltd. and Atheneum Publishing; on page 93, Cassell and Co. Ltd. and The University of Oklahoma Press.